RECORDED VERSIONS
GUITAR

AUTHENTIC TRANSCRIPTIONS
WITH NOTES AND TABLATURE

Good Charlotte — the Young and the Hopeless

Music transcriptions by Colin Higgins, Jeff Jacobson, Paul Pappas, David Stocker and Jeff Story

ISBN 1-84328-425-1

International Music Publications Limited
Griffin House, 161 Hammersmith Road, London W6 8BS, England

A New Beginning

Words and Music by Benjamin Combs and Eric Dodd

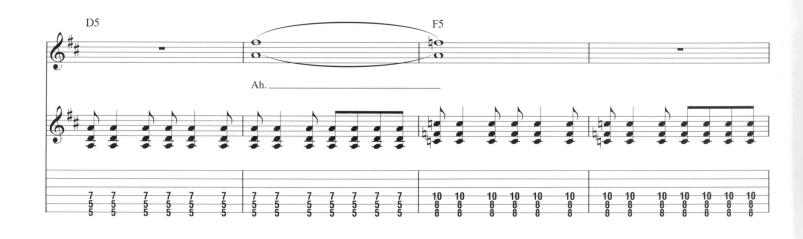

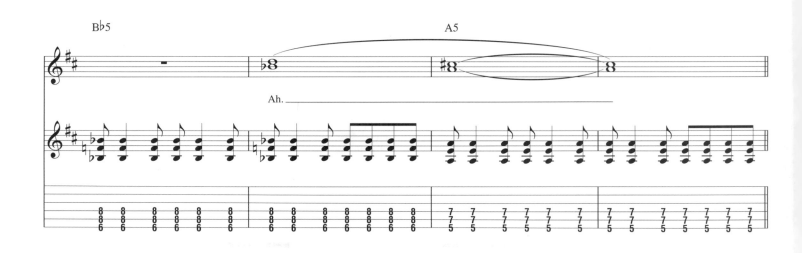

D

Gtr. 7: w/ Rhy. Fig. 1

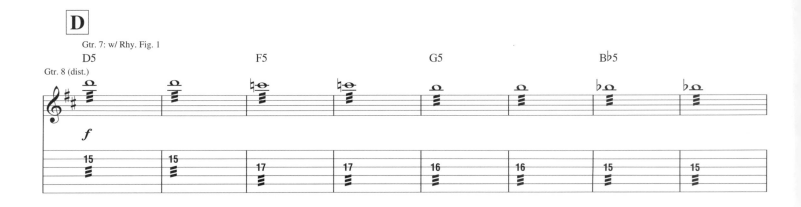

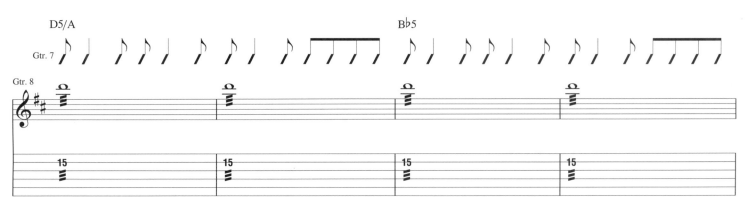

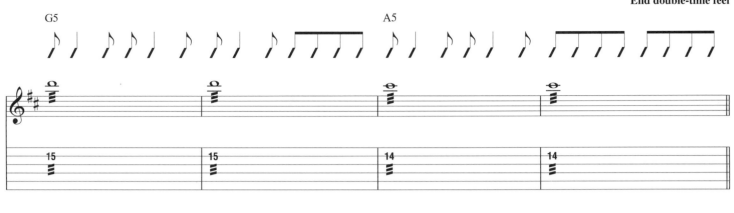

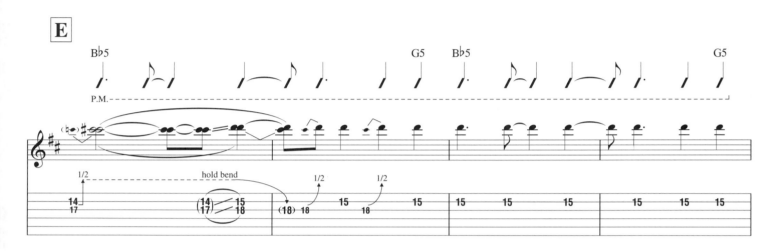

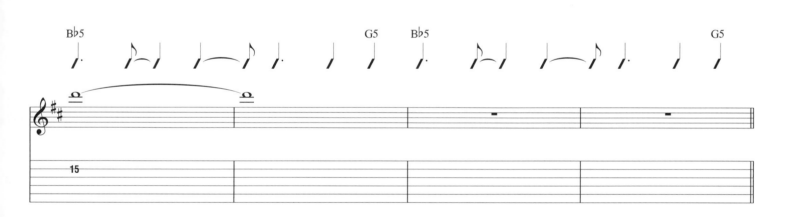

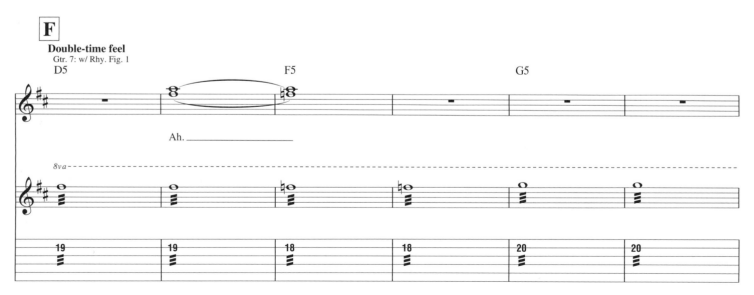

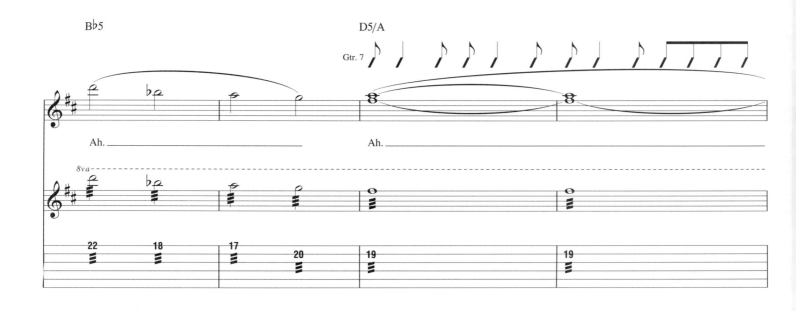

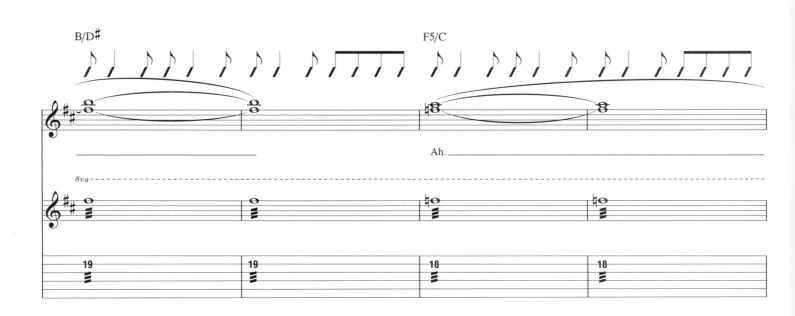

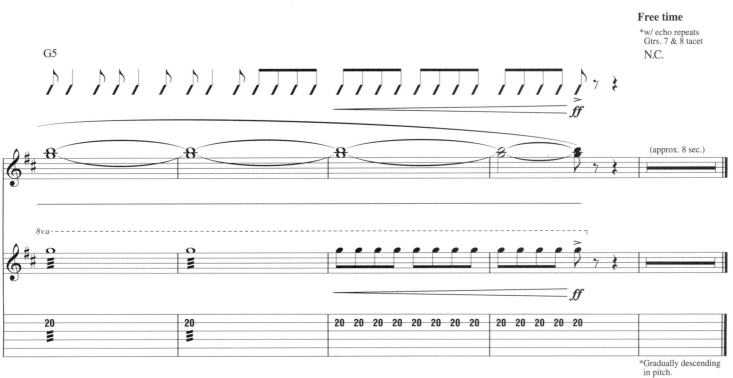

*Gradually descending
in pitch.

The Anthem

Words and Music by Benjamin Combs, Joel Combs and John Feldman

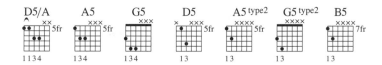

Tune down 1/2 step:
(low to high) Eb-Ab-Db-Gb-Bb-Eb

Intro

Moderately fast Rock ♩ = 180

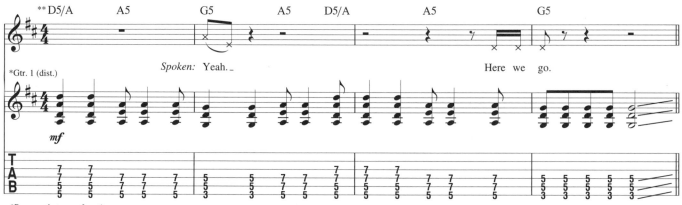

*Processed gtr. arr. for gtr.

**Chord symbols reflect overall harmony.

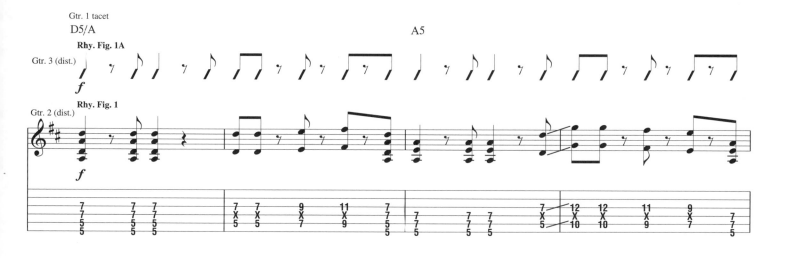

Verse

new day, but it all feels old. It's a good life, that's what I'm told. But

ev-'ry - thing,_ it all_ just feels_ the same._____ And my

Gtr. 2 tacet
Gtr. 3: w/ Rhy. Fig. 2

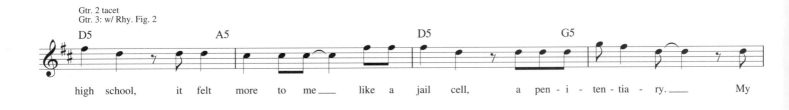

high school, it felt more to me __ like a jail cell, a pen - i - ten - tia - ry.__ My

Gtr. 2: w/ Rhy. Fig. 3

time spent there, it on - ly made_ me see _____ that

Coda

Bridge

don't wan-na be you. Shake it once, _____ that's fine. _____

Shake it twice, _____ that's o - kay.   Shake it three _____

_____ times, _____ you're play - ing with _____ your - self _____ a - gain.

Interlude

12

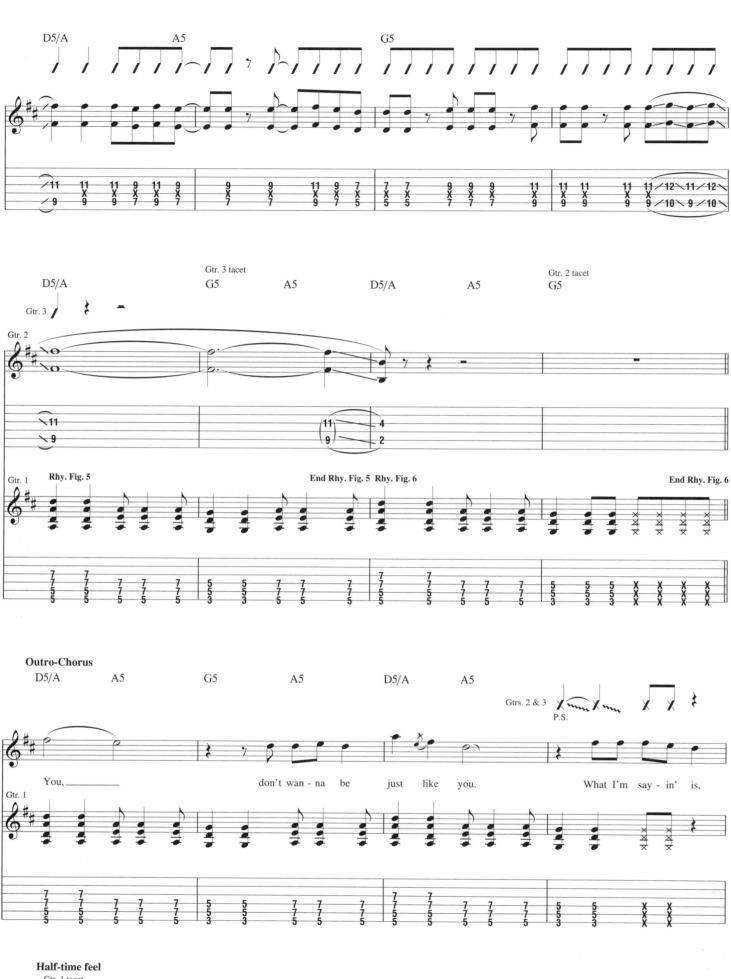

You, _____ don't wan - na be just like you. (Don't wan - na be just like you.)

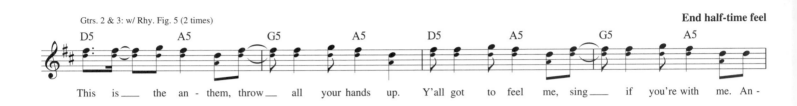

This is ___ the an - them, throw ___ all your hands up. Y'all got to feel me, sing ___ if you're with me. An -

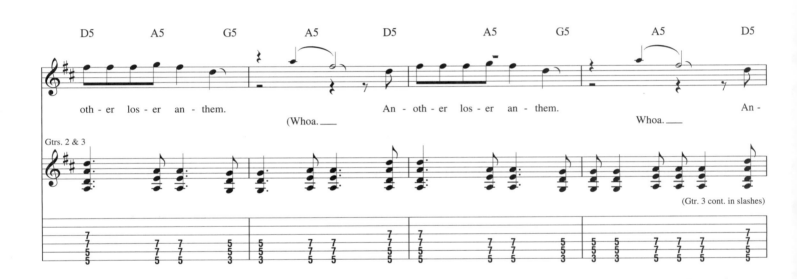

oth - er los - er an - them. (Whoa. ___ An - oth - er los - er an - them. Whoa. ___ An -

(Gtr. 3 cont. in slashes)

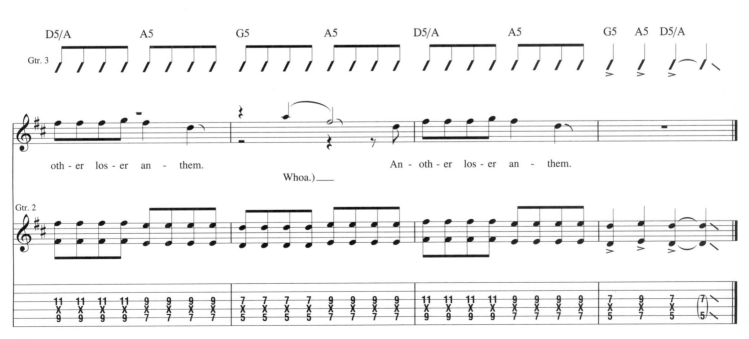

oth - er los - er an - them. Whoa.) ___ An - oth - er los - er an - them.

Lifestyles of the Rich and Famous

Words and Music by Benjamin Combs and Joel Combs

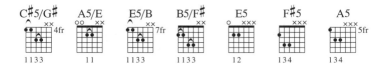

Tune down 1 1/2 steps:
(low to high) Db-Gb-B-E-Ab-Db

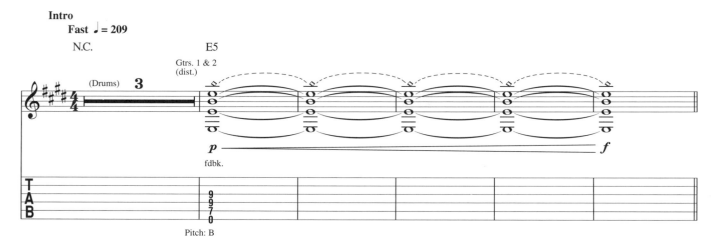

Verse

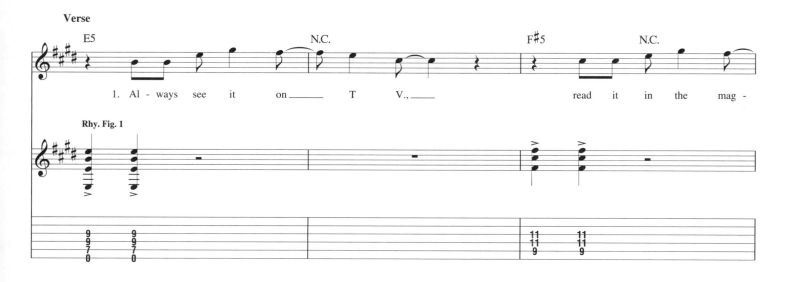

1. Al - ways see it on T V., read it in the mag -

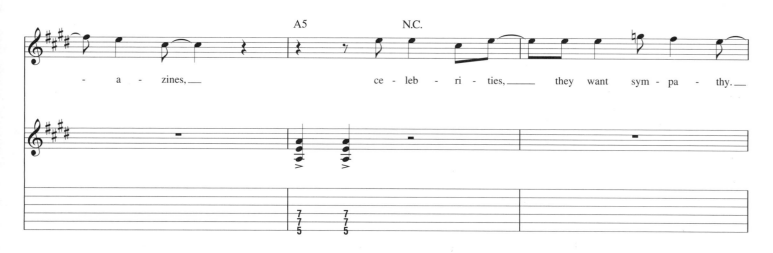

- a - zines, ce - leb - ri - ties, they want sym - pa - thy.

-lem, well, they got man - sions,

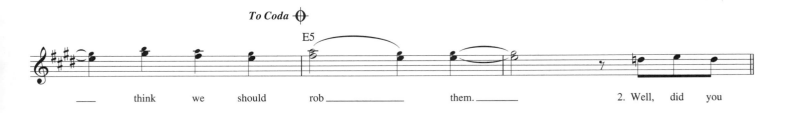

To Coda ⊕

___ think we should rob ___ them. ___ 2. Well, did you

Verse

Gtr. 1: w/ Rhy. Fig. 1 (1 1/2 times)
Gtr. 2: w/ Rhy. Fig. 1 (2 times)

know when you are fa - mous you could kill your wife, ___ and there's no such thing as twen - ty -

five to life ___ as long as you got the cash ___ to pay for Coch -

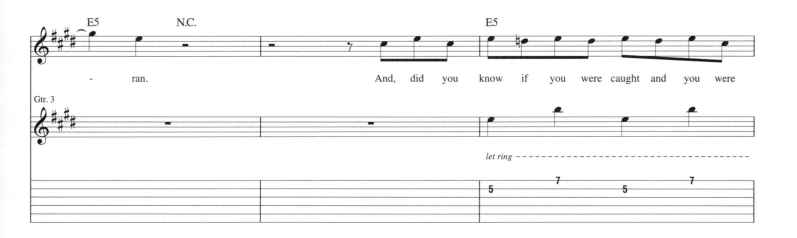

- ran. And, did you know if you were caught and you were

Gtr. 3

let ring -

smok - in' crack, ___ Mc - Don - ald's would - n't e - ven wan - na take you back, ___ you could

let ring -

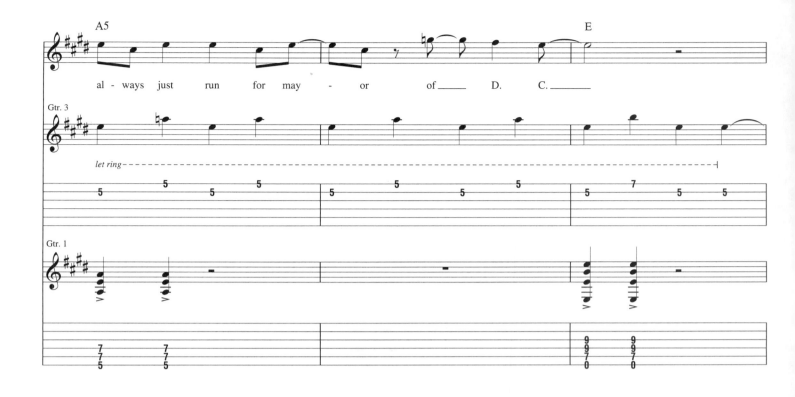

Pre-Chorus
Gtr. 3: w/ Riff A

*Pick eighth-note triplets while sliding down 6th string.

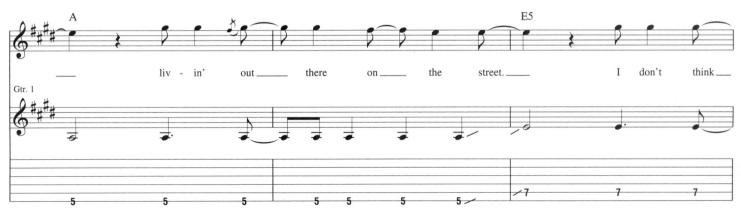

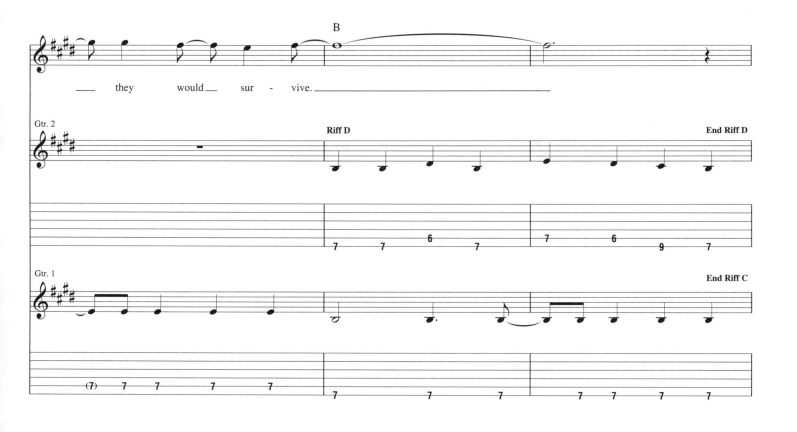

they would sur - vive.

Gtr. 2
Riff D
End Riff D

Gtr. 1
End Riff C

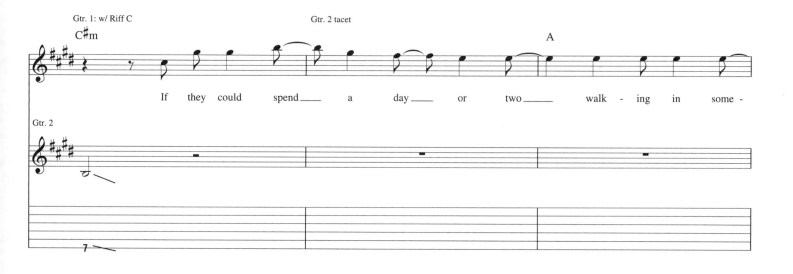

Gtr. 1: w/ Riff C

C#m

Gtr. 2 tacet

A

If they could spend a day or two walk - ing in some -

Gtr. 2

E5

- one else - 's shoes, I think they'd stum -

Gtr. 2: w/ Riff D

B

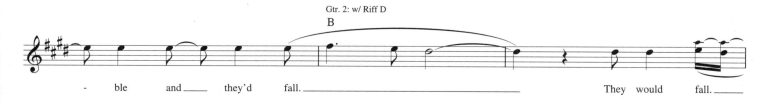

- ble and they'd fall. They would fall.

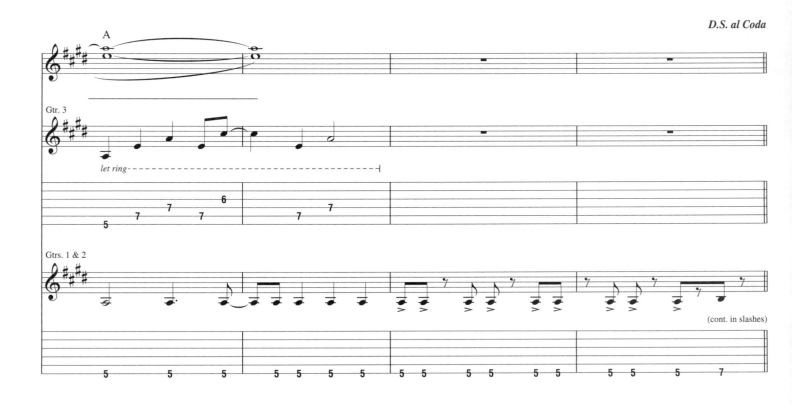

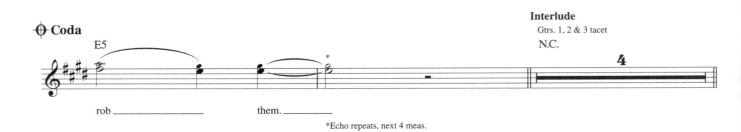

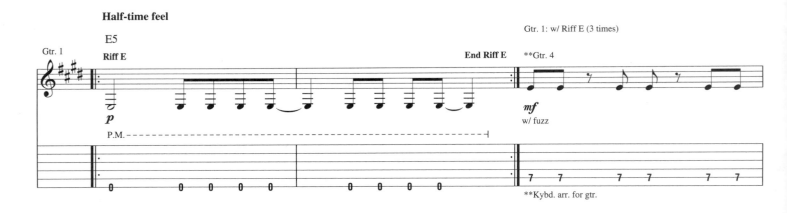

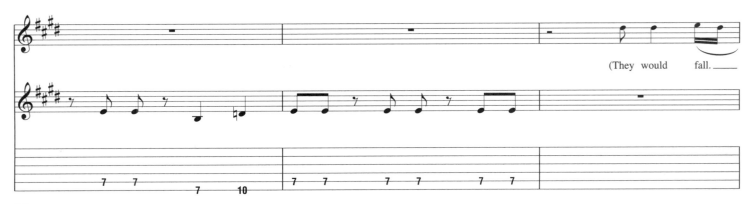

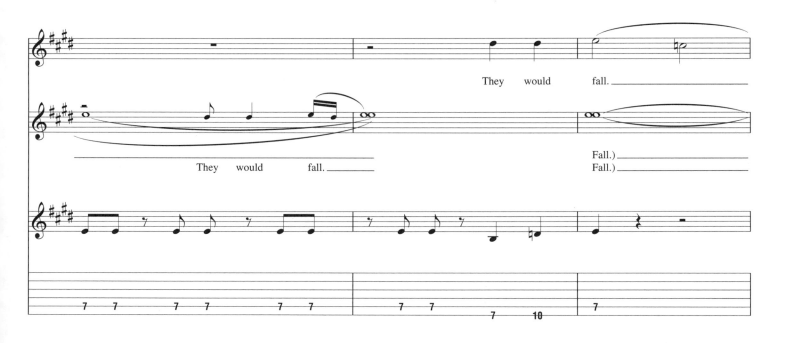

Chorus

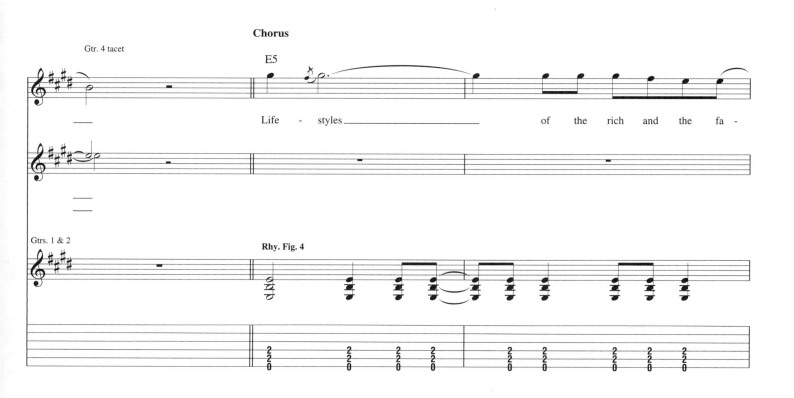

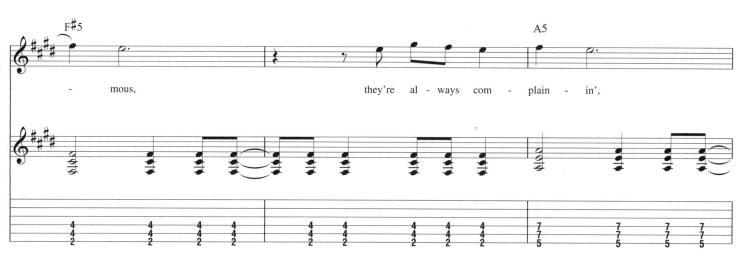

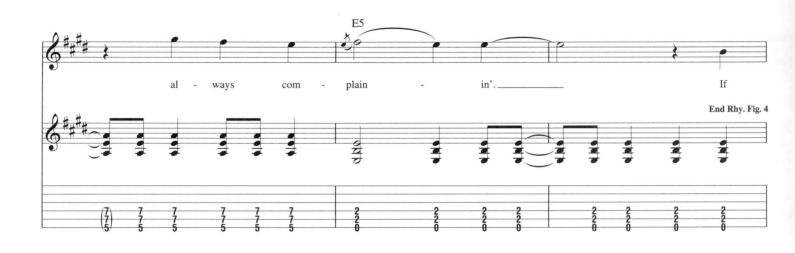

al - ways com - plain - in'._____ If

End Rhy. Fig. 4

Gtrs. 1 & 2: w/ Rhy. Fig. 4

mon - ey_____ is such a prob - lem, we got so man - y prob-

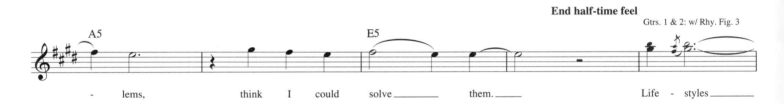

End half-time feel

Gtrs. 1 & 2: w/ Rhy. Fig. 3

- lems, think I could solve_____ them._____ Life - styles_____

_____ of the rich and the fa - mous,_____ we'll take their

clothes, cash, cars, and homes_____ just stop com - plain - in'.

Outro

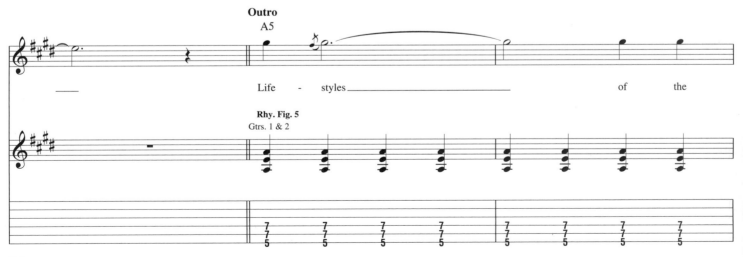

Life - styles_____ of the

Rhy. Fig. 5
Gtrs. 1 & 2

24

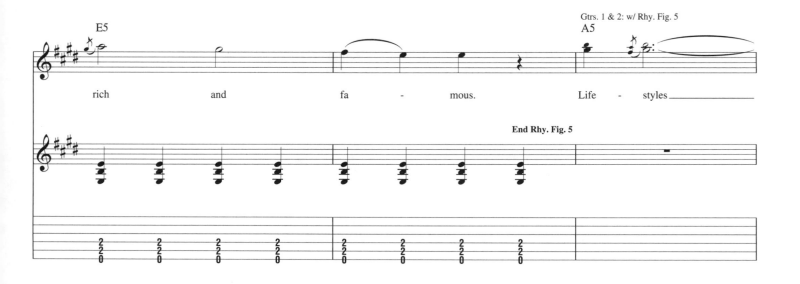

rich   and   fa -   mous.   Life - styles

_____   of   the   rich   and   fa -   mous.

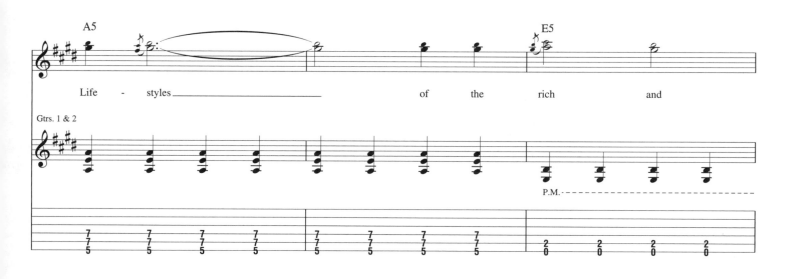

Life - styles _____   of   the   rich   and

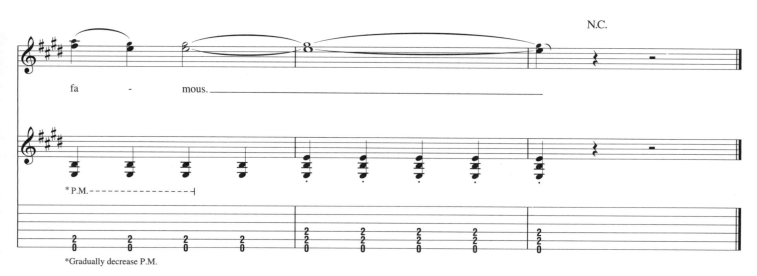

fa -   mous. _____

*Gradually decrease P.M.

Wondering

Words and Music by Benjamin Combs and Joel Combs

Interlude

Verse

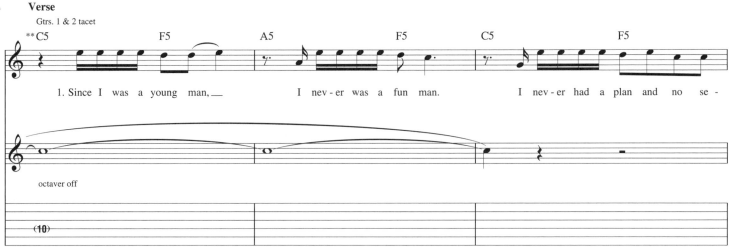

**Chord symbols reflect implied harmony.

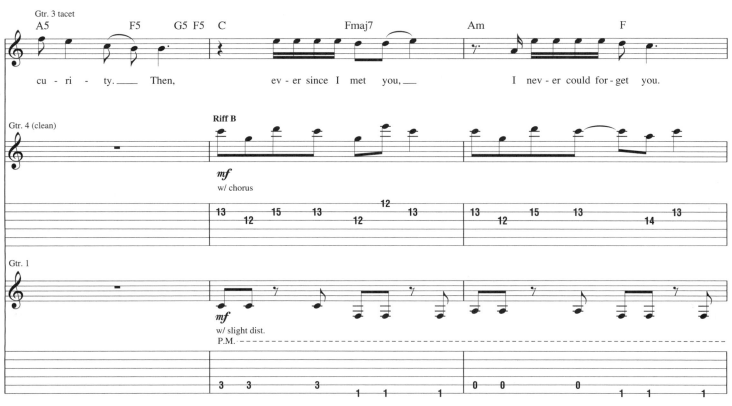

Chorus

Gtrs. 1 & 2: w/ Rhy. Fig. 1

I ___ found ___ just in ___ time. _____ If you tell me to wait, ___

___ I will wait for you. ___ If you tell me to stay, ___ I would stay right through. ___

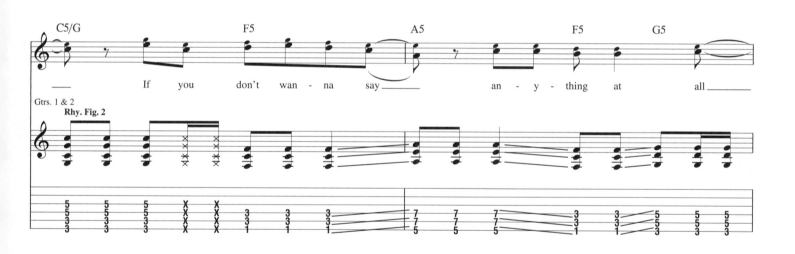

___ If you don't wan - na say _____ an - y - thing at all _____

Gtrs. 1 & 2

Rhy. Fig. 2

To Coda ⊕

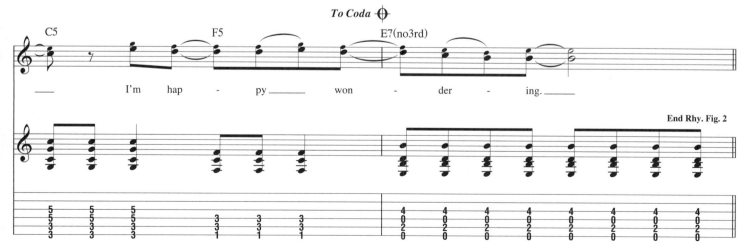

___ I'm hap - py ___ won - der - ing. ___

End Rhy. Fig. 2

Coda

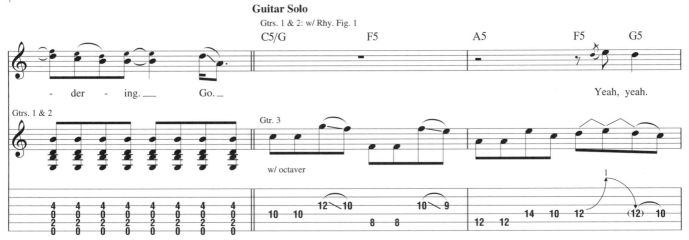

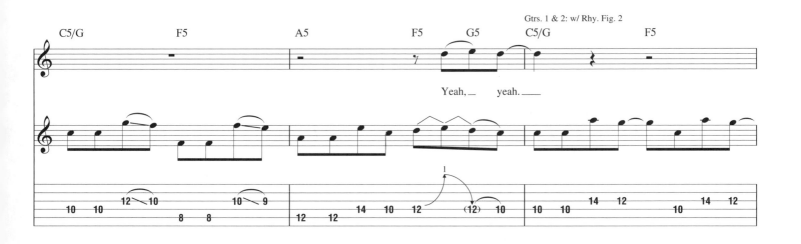

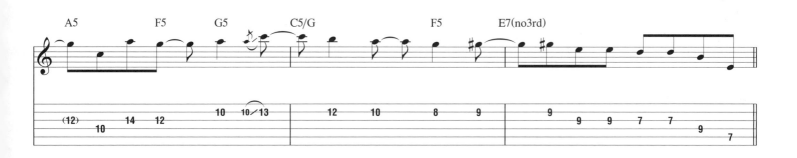

Bridge

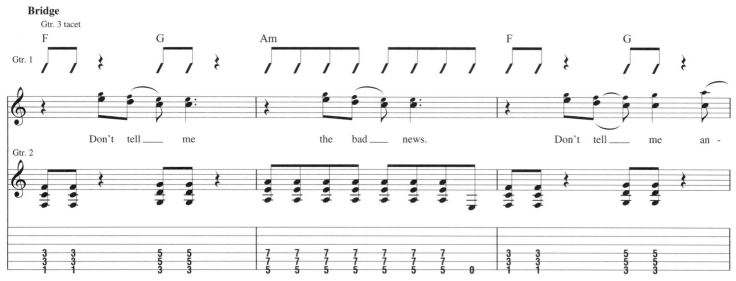

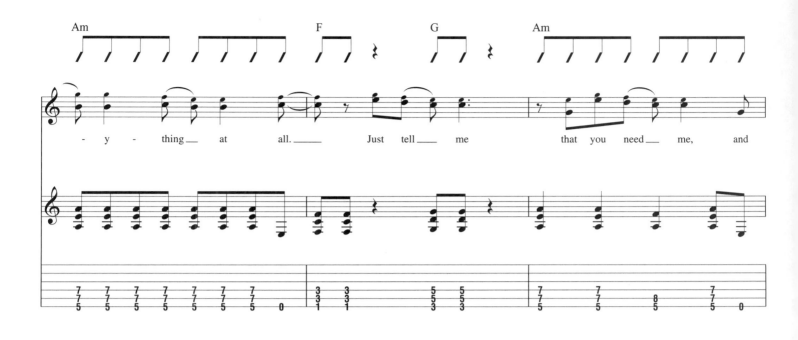

-y - thing___ at all.___ Just tell___ me that you need___ me, and

Chorus
Gtr. 1: w/ Riff A

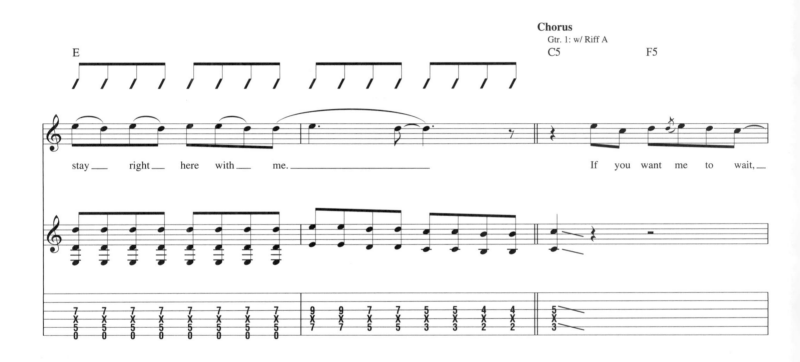

stay___ right___ here with___ me._____ If you want me to wait,

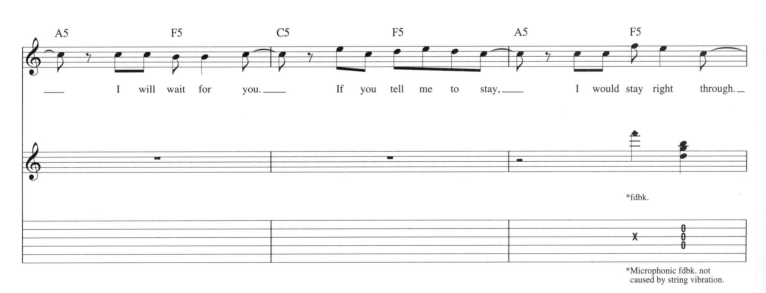

___ I will wait for you.___ If you tell me to stay,___ I would stay right through.___

*fdbk.

*Microphonic fdbk. not
caused by string vibration.

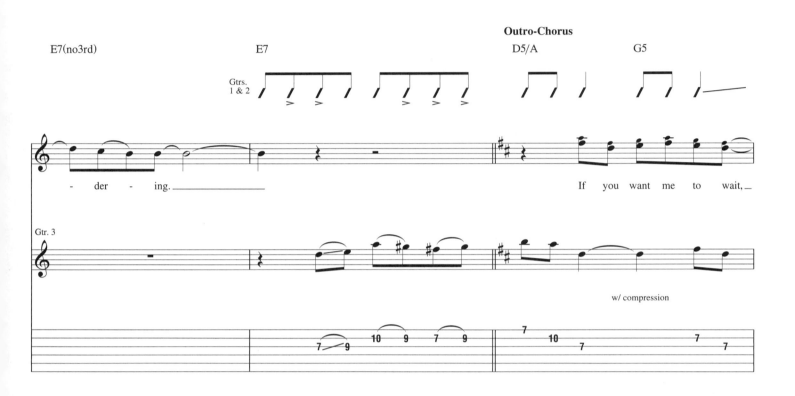

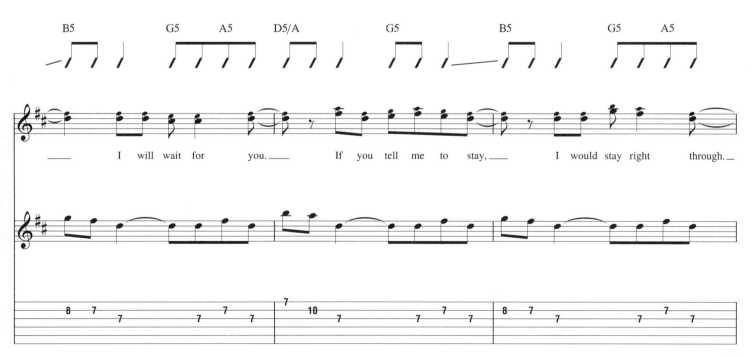

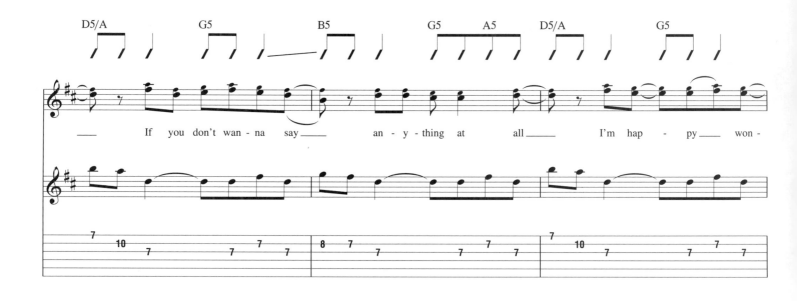

If you don't wan-na say _____ an-y-thing at all _____ I'm hap-py _____ won-

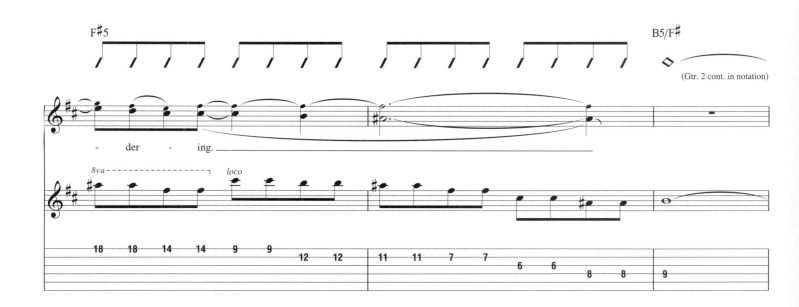

-der _____ ing. _____

(Gtr. 2 cont. in notation)

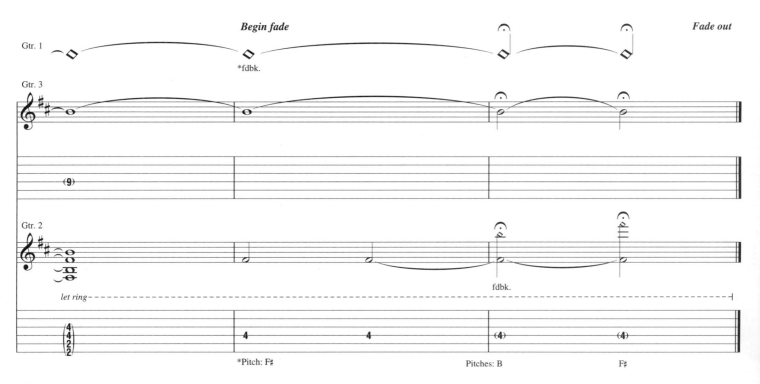

*Pitch: F#   Pitches: B   F#

The Story of My Old Man

Words and Music by Benjamin Combs and Joel Combs

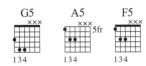

Tune down 1/2 step:
(low to high) Eb-Ab-Db-Gb-Bb-Eb

Intro
Fast Punk ♩ = 270

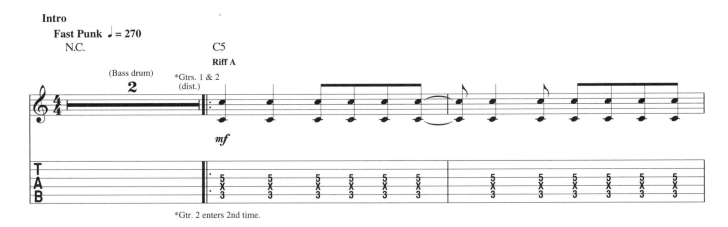

*Gtr. 2 enters 2nd time.

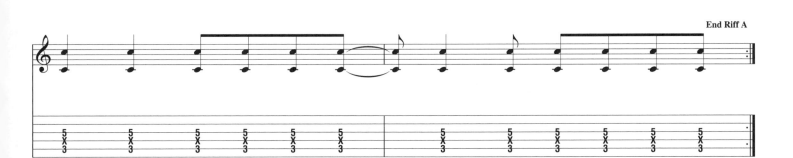

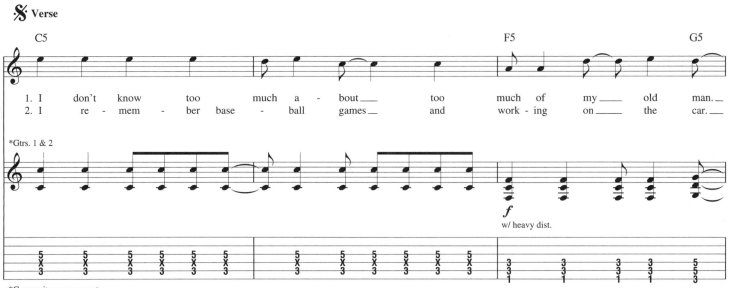

*Composite arrangement

Thurs - day _____ through Sat - ur - day, _____ lost ev - 'ry -

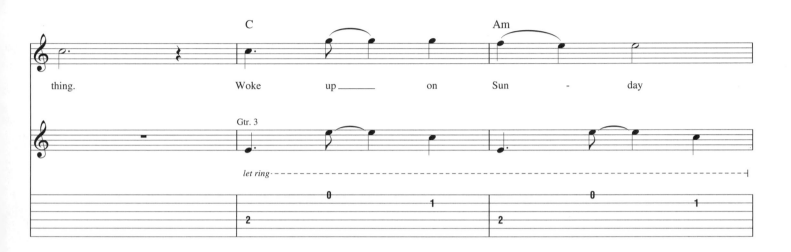

thing. Woke up _____ on Sun - day

Gtr. 3

let ring -

D.S. al Coda

Interlude

End half-time feel

Gtr. 3 tacet

Gtrs. 1 & 2: w/ Riff A

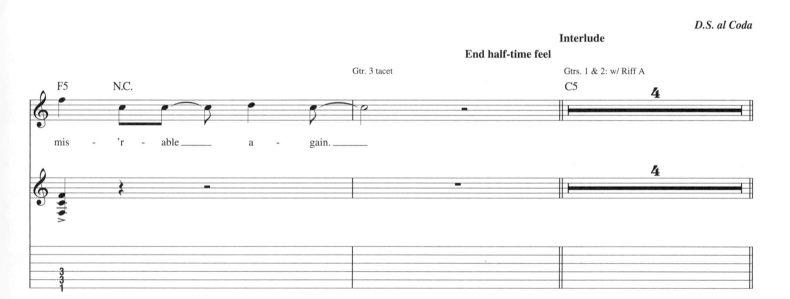

mis - 'r - able _____ a - gain. _____

 Coda

Gtr. 2: w/ Rhy. Fig. 1 (last 2 meas.)

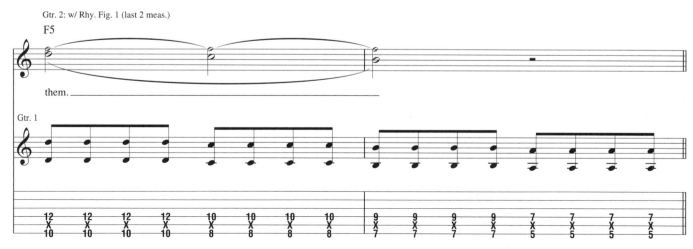

them. _____

Gtr. 1

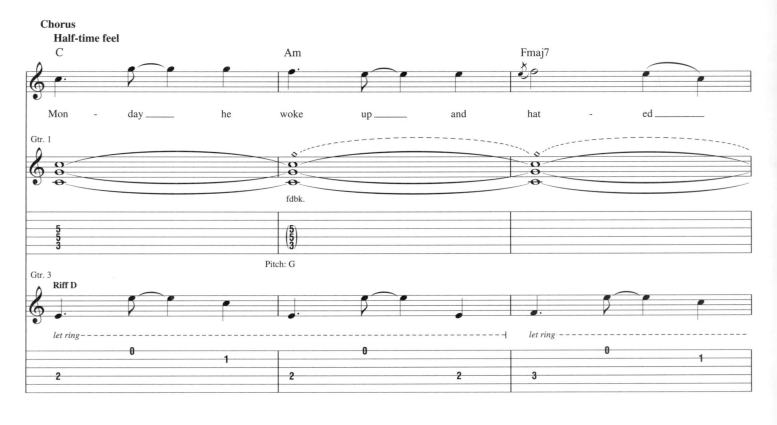

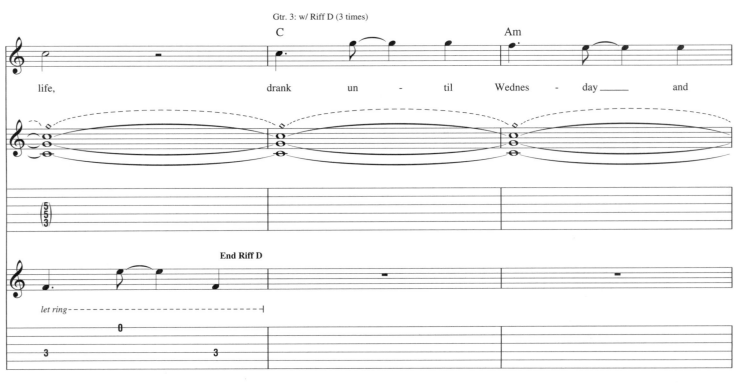

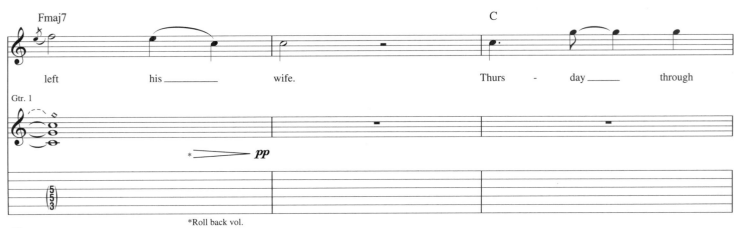

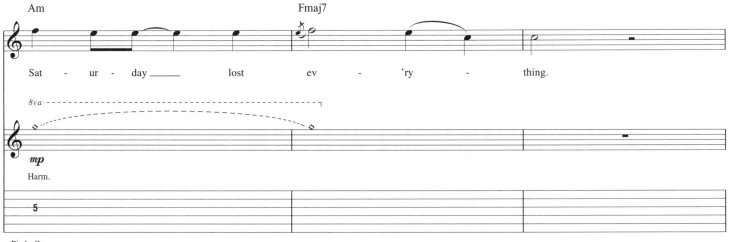

Sat - ur - day _____ lost ev - 'ry - thing.

8va

mp

Harm.

Pitch: G

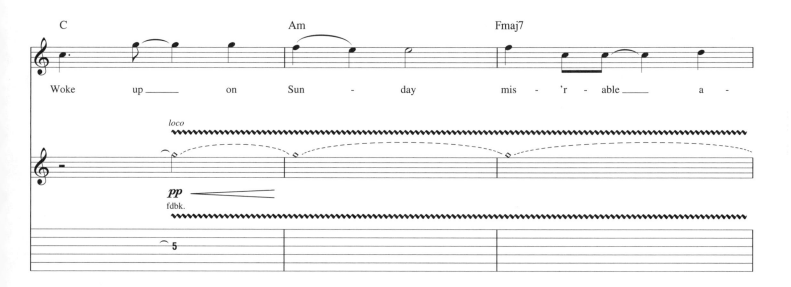

Woke up _____ on Sun - day mis - 'r - able _____ a -

loco

pp
fdbk.

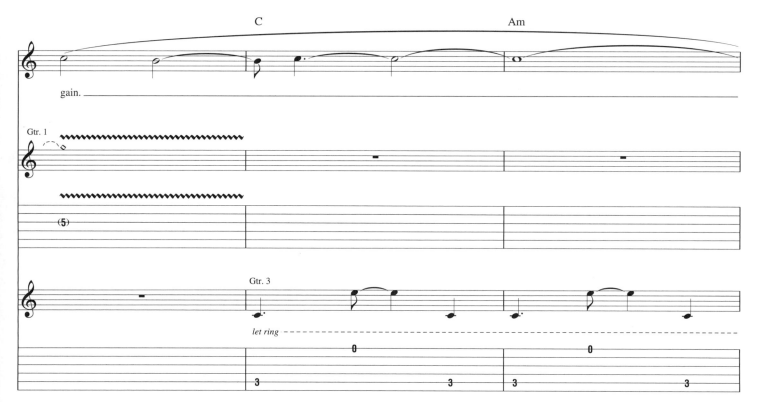

gain. _____

Gtr. 1

Gtr. 3

let ring -

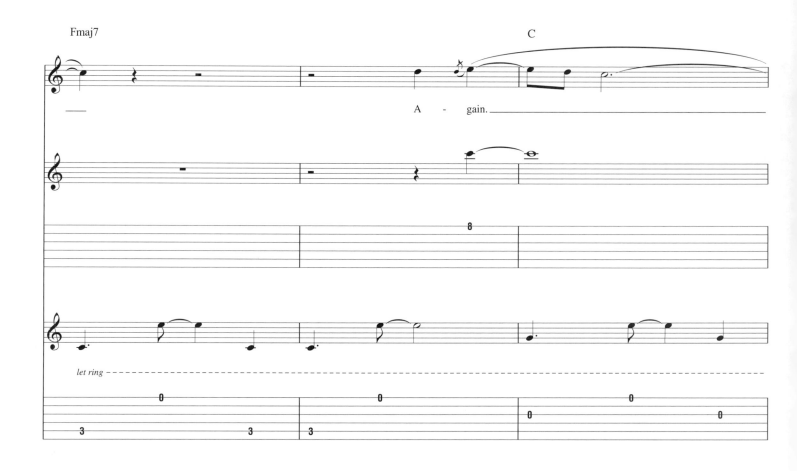

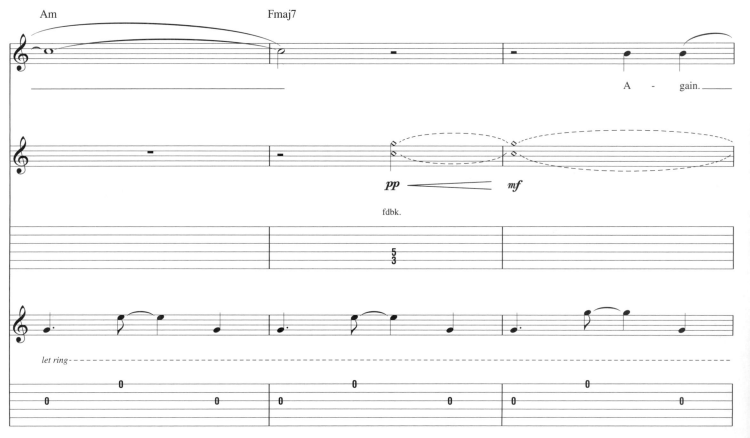

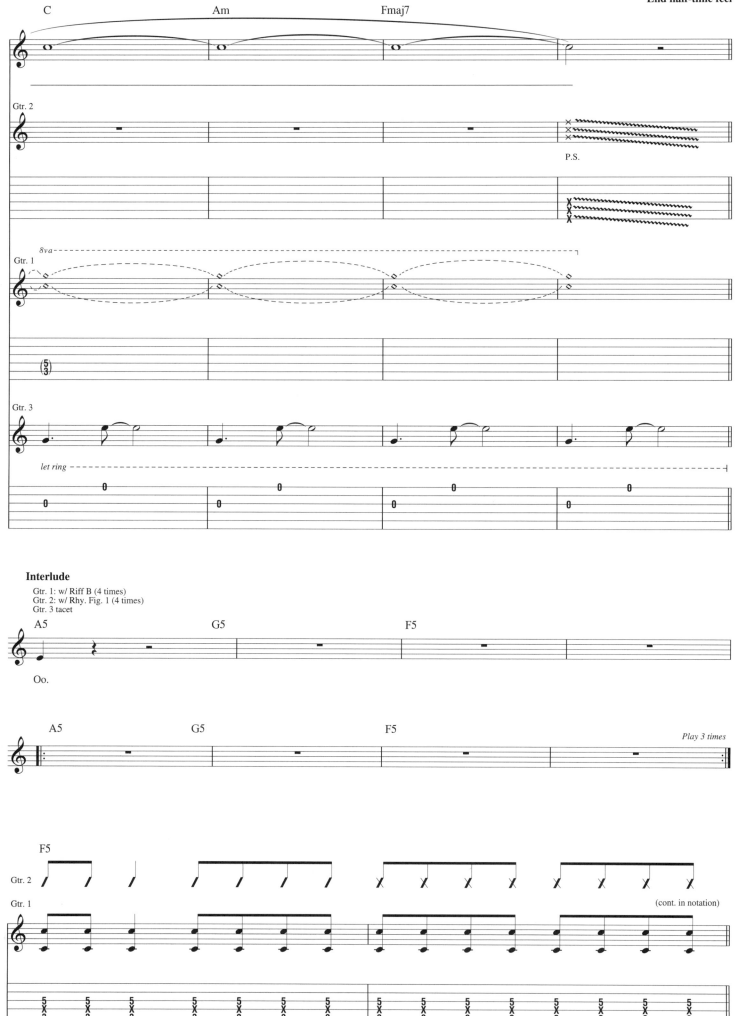

Outro-Chorus

Some - day __ we'll wish that __ he made things __

right,
(Made things __

long for __ his fam - 'ly __ and

right.)

miss his __ wife.
Miss his __ wife.

Re - mem - ber __ the

days he __ had ev - 'ry - thing.
Ev - 'ry -

Now he's a - lone and mis - 'r - able a - gain. __
thing.) __

Girls & Boys

Words and Music by Benjamin Combs and Joel Combs

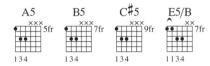

Tune down 1/2 step:
(low to high) E♭-A♭-D♭-G♭-B♭-E♭

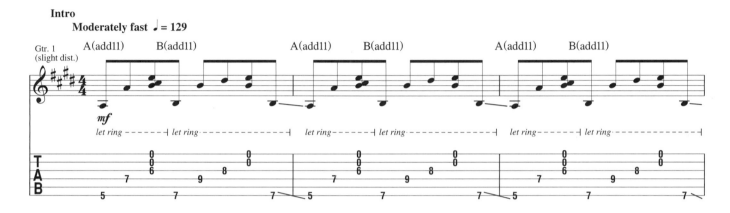

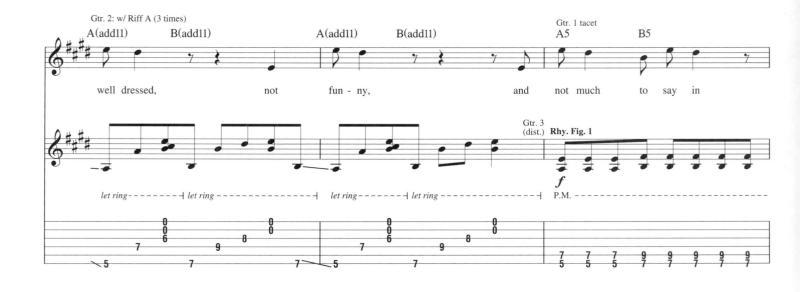

well dressed,   not   fun - ny,   and   not much   to   say in

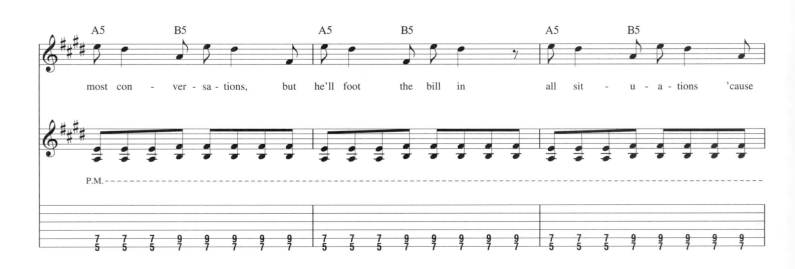

most con - ver - sa - tions,   but   he'll   foot   the   bill   in   all   sit - u - a - tions   'cause

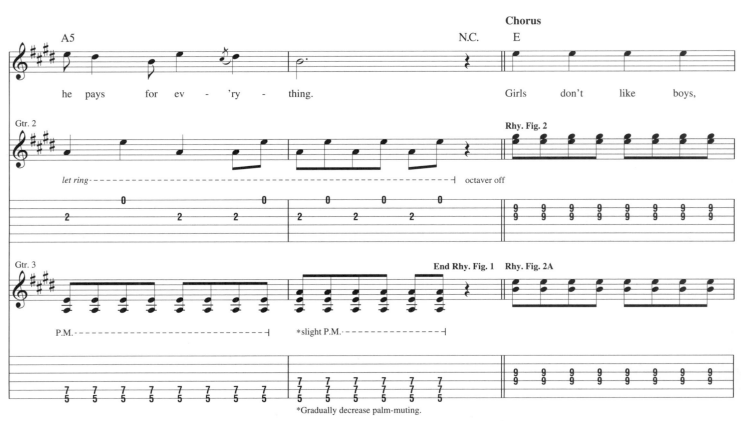

he   pays   for   ev - 'ry - thing.   Girls   don't   like   boys,

*Gradually decrease palm-muting.

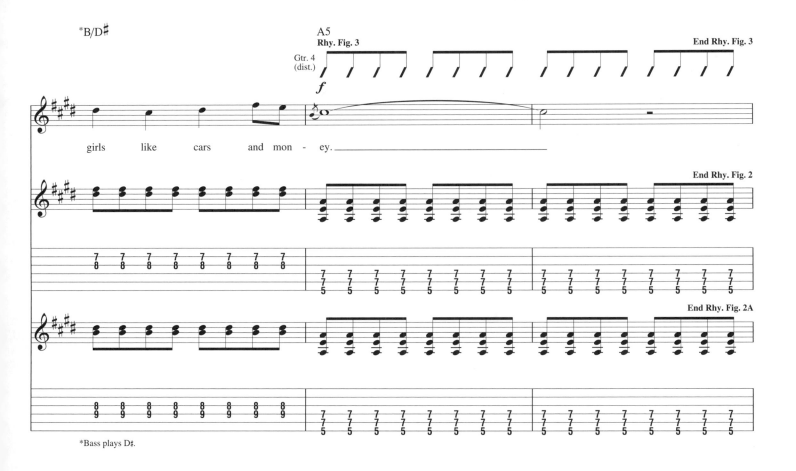

girls like cars and mon - ey. _____

*Bass plays D♯.

Boys will laugh at girls when they're ___ not fun - ny. _____

Verse

Gtrs. 3 & 4 tacet

2. Pa - per, or plas - tic, don't

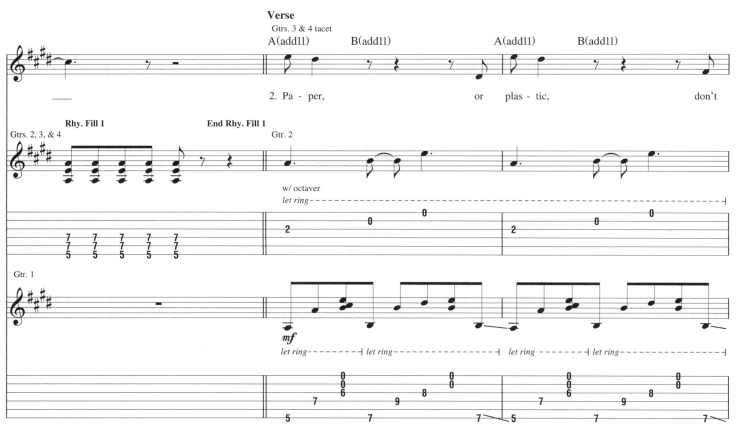

Chorus

Gtrs. 2 & 3: w/ Rhy. Figs. 2 & 2A (3 3/4 times)

Gtr. 4: w/ Rhy. Fig. 3

E   *B/D#   A5

Girls   don't   like   boys,   girls   like   cars   and   mon - ey. _____

*Bass plays D#.

E   B/D#

_____ Boys   will   laugh   at   girls   when   they're __ not   fun -

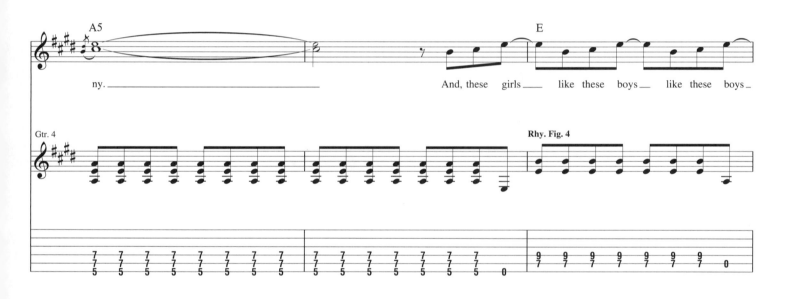

A5   E

ny. _____ And, these   girls __ like   these   boys __ like   these   boys __

Gtr. 4

Rhy. Fig. 4

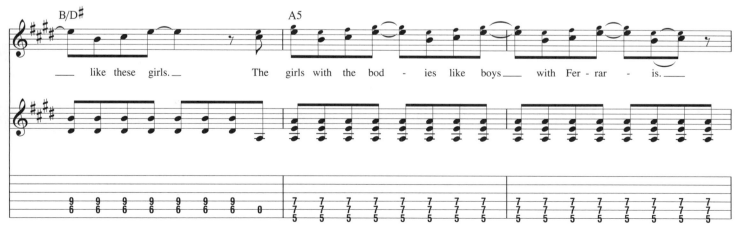

B/D#   A5

_ like   these   girls. _ The   girls   with   the   bod - ies   like   boys __ with   Fer - rar - is. _

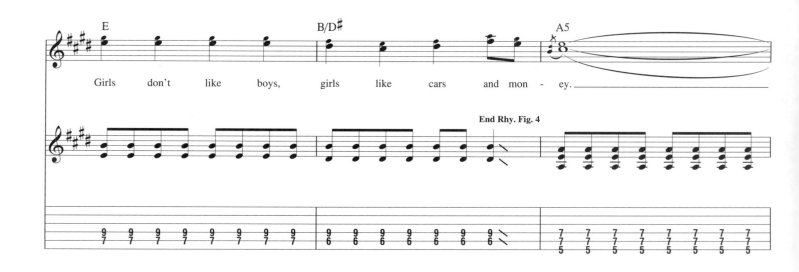

Girls don't like boys, girls like cars and mon - ey.

End Rhy. Fig. 4

Interlude

Gtrs. 2, 3 & 4: w/ Rhy. Fill 1

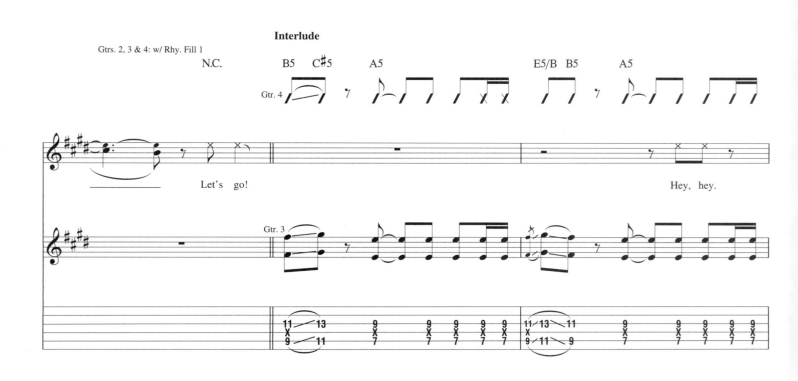

Let's go!

Hey, hey.

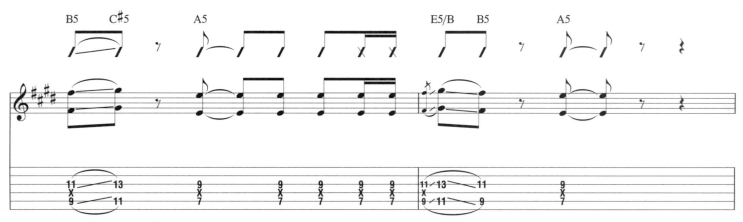

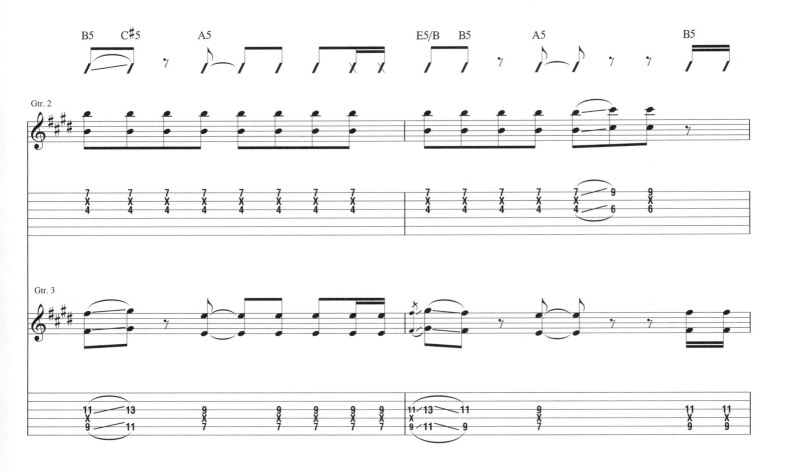

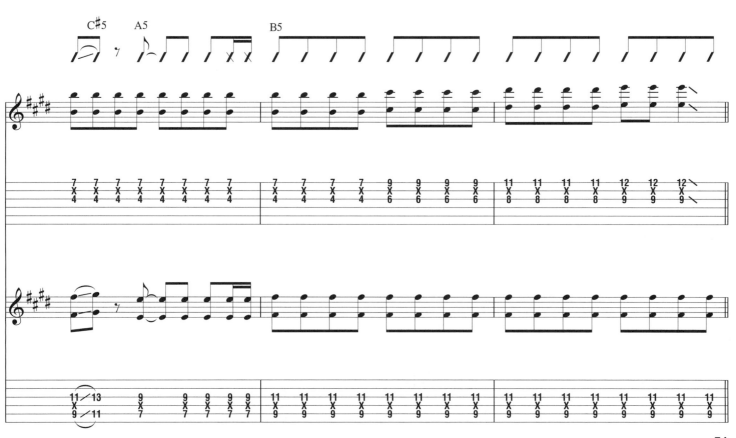

Chorus

*Bass plays D#.

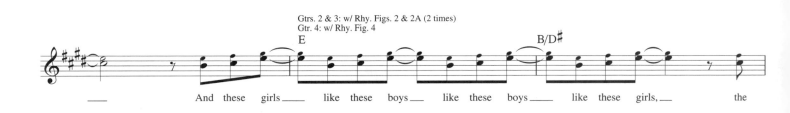

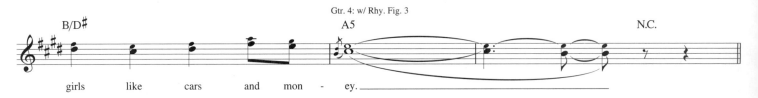

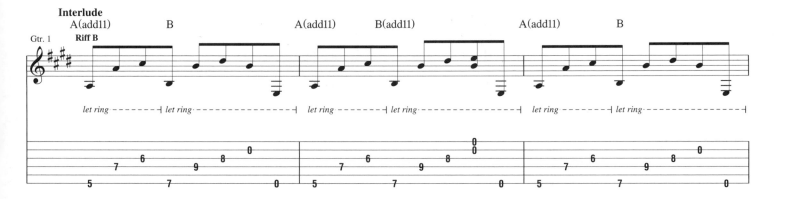

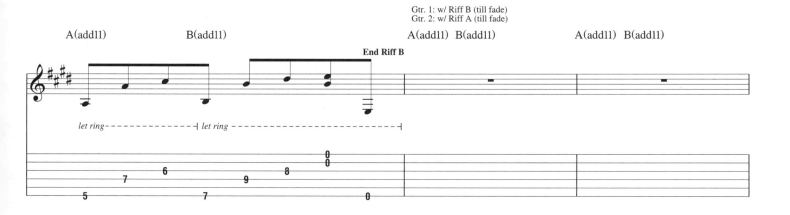

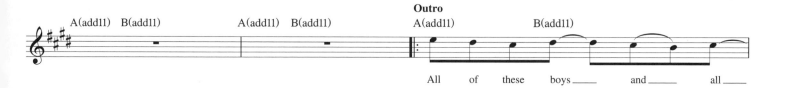

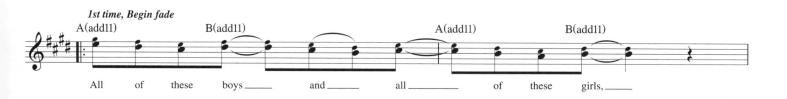

My Bloody Valentine

Words and Music by Benjamin Combs and Joel Combs

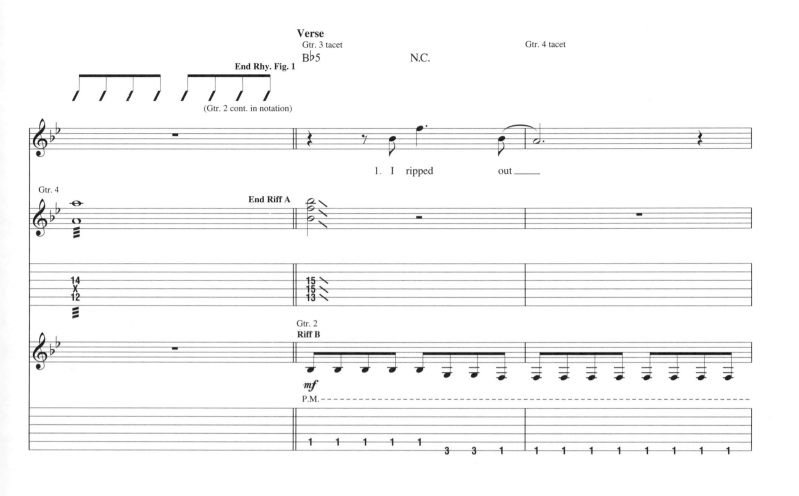

his   throat,_____   and   called   you_____

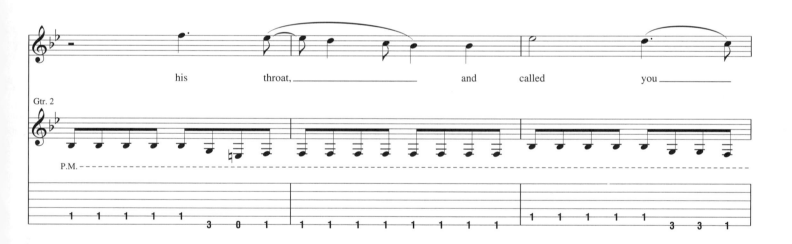

on _____   the   tel   -   e   -   phone _____   to

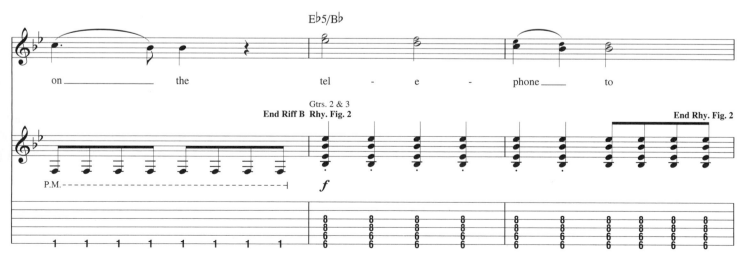

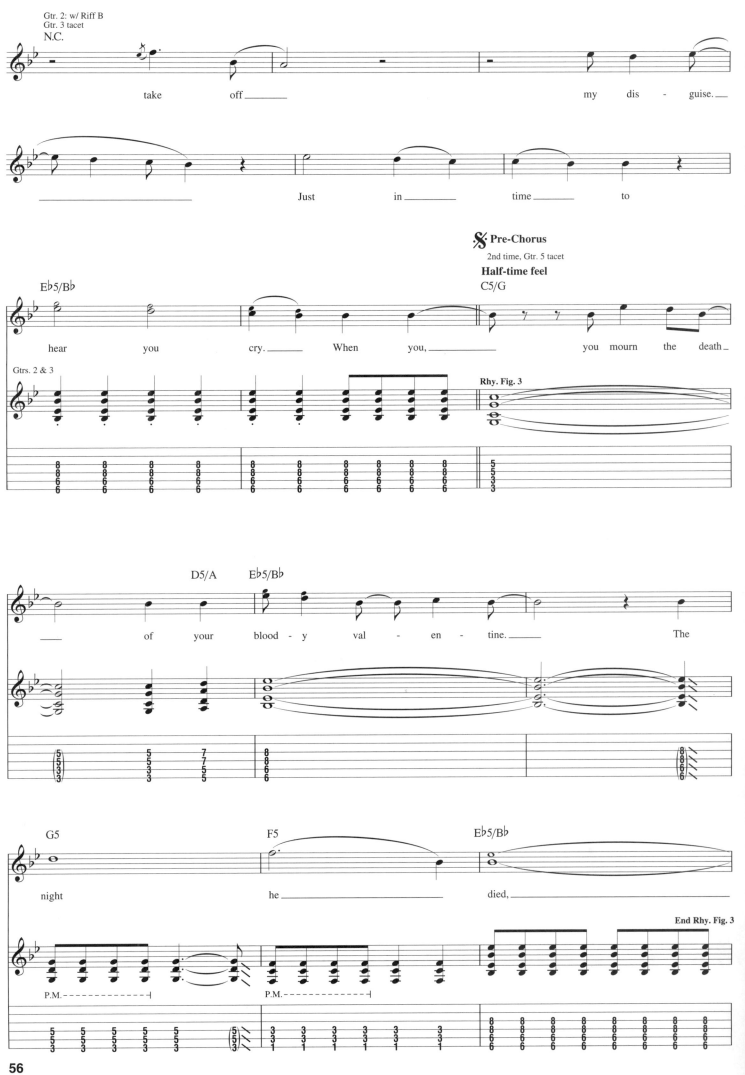

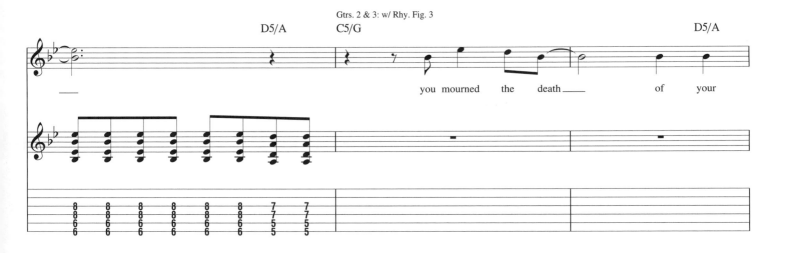

you mourned the death ____ of your

blood - y val - en - tine ____ one ____

End half-time feel

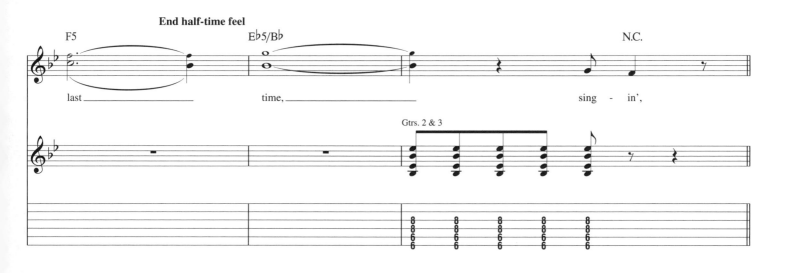

last ____ time, ____ sing - in',

𝄌𝄌 Chorus

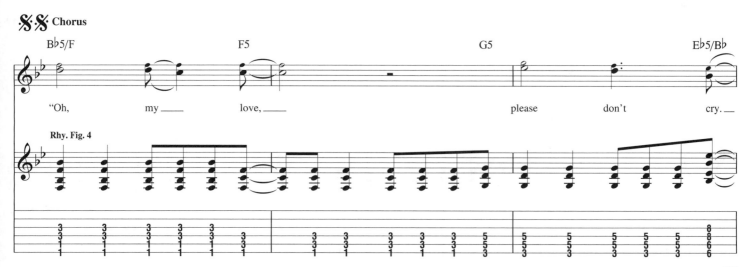

"Oh, my ____ love, ____ please don't cry. ____

Rhy. Fig. 4

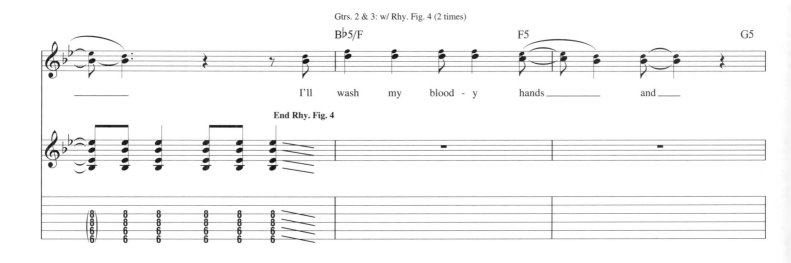

I'll wash my blood - y hands _____ and _____

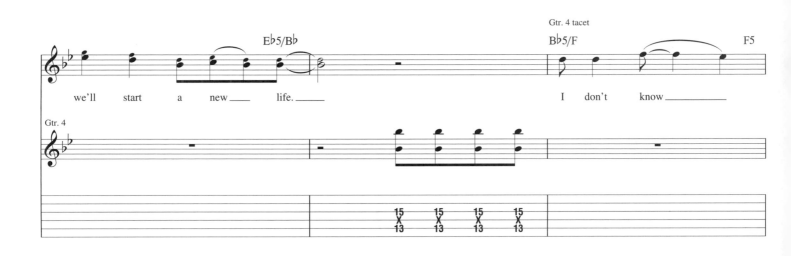

we'll start a new _____ life. _____   I don't know _____

much at all. _____   I don't know _____ wrong from right. _____

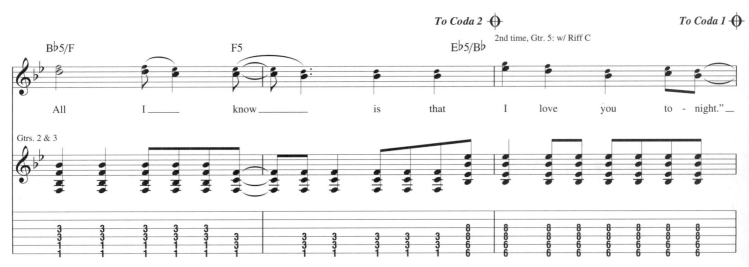

All   I _____ know _____ is that I love you to - night." _____

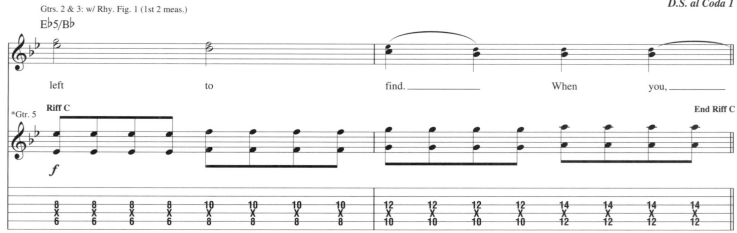

*Strings arr. for gtr.

Coda 1

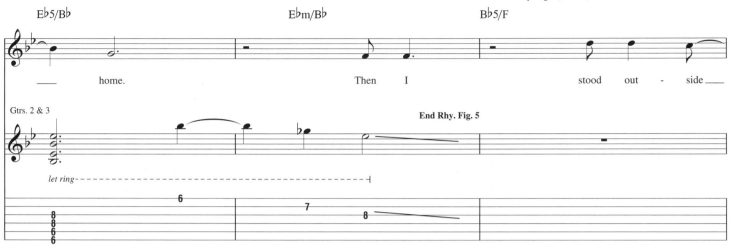

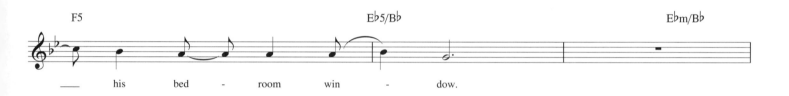

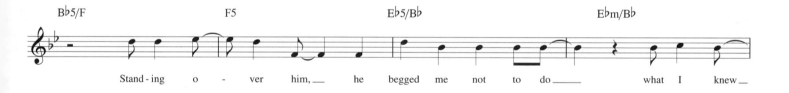

Coda 2

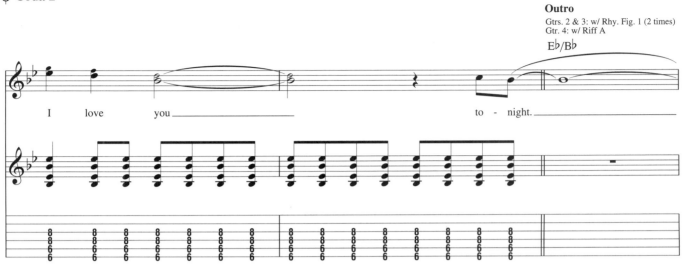

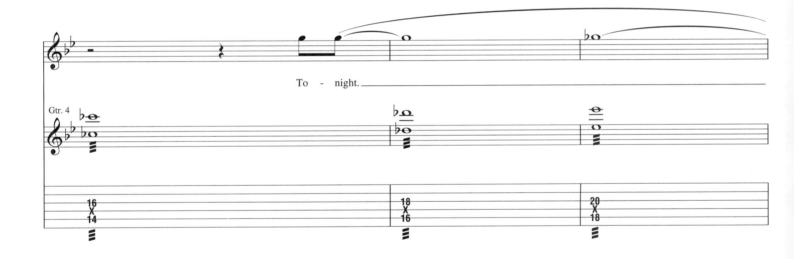

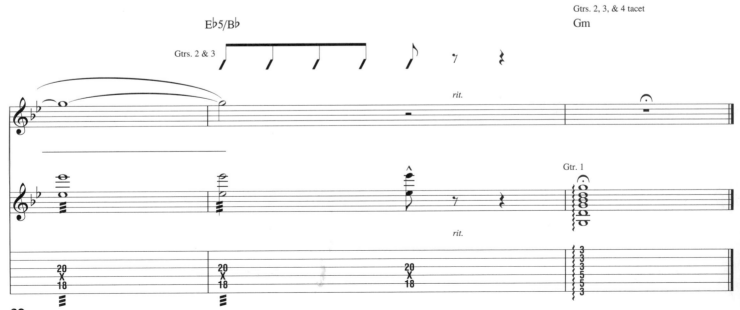

Hold On

Words and Music by Benjamin Combs and Joel Combs

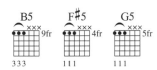

*Drop D tuning, down 1/2 step:
(low to high) Db-Ab-Db-Gb-Bb-Eb

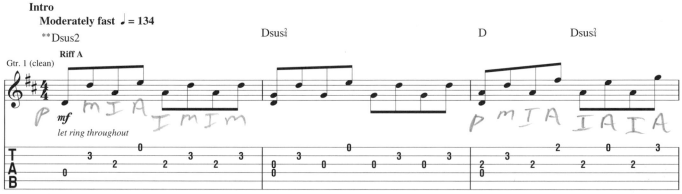

**Chord symbols reflect implied harmony.
*Recording sounds an additional ¼ step flat.

***Chord symbols reflect combined harmony.

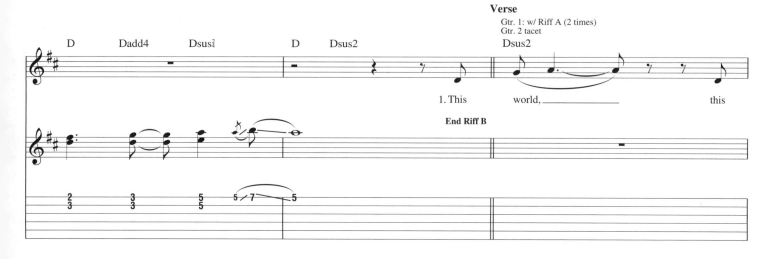

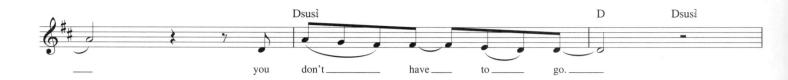

you don't _____ have _____ to _____ go. _____

Gtr. 1: w/ Riff A (2 times)
Gtr. 2: w/ Riff B (2 times)

You're feel - ing sad, _____ you're feel - ing lone - ly and

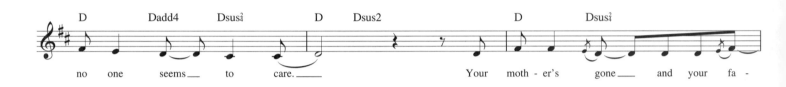

no one seems _____ to care. _____ Your moth - er's gone _____ and your fa -

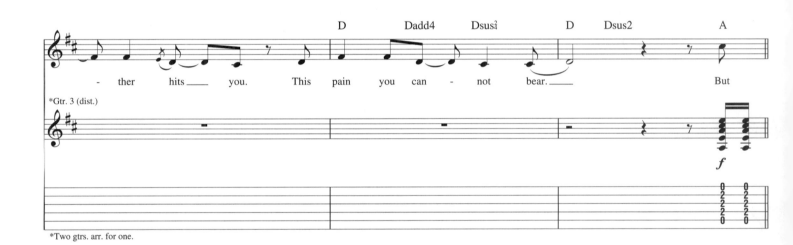

- ther hits _____ you. This pain you can - not bear. _____ But

*Gtr. 3 (dist.)

*Two gtrs. arr. for one.

§ **Pre-Chorus**

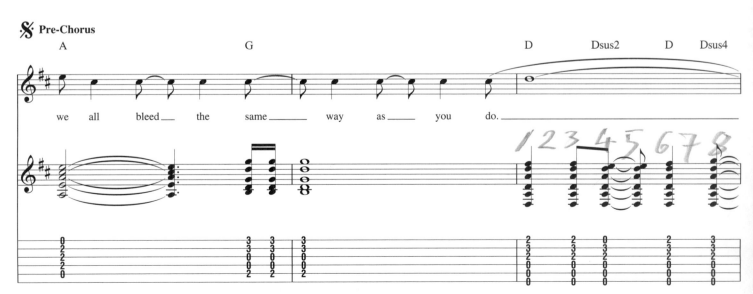

we all bleed _____ the same _____ way as _____ you do. _____

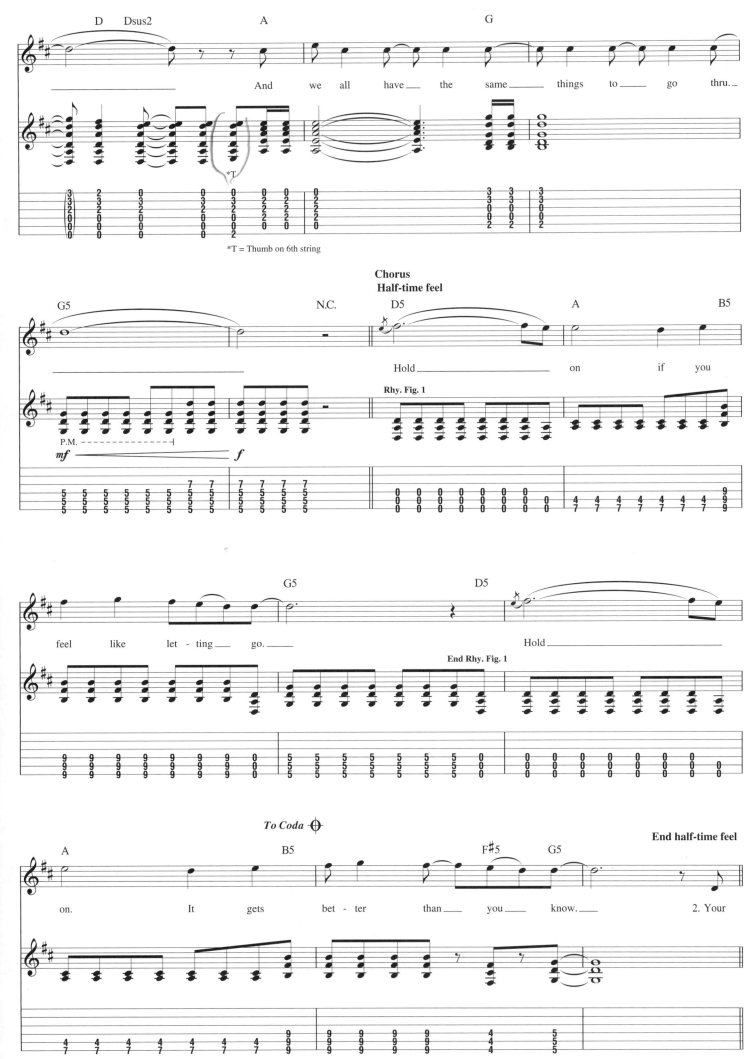

*T = Thumb on 6th string

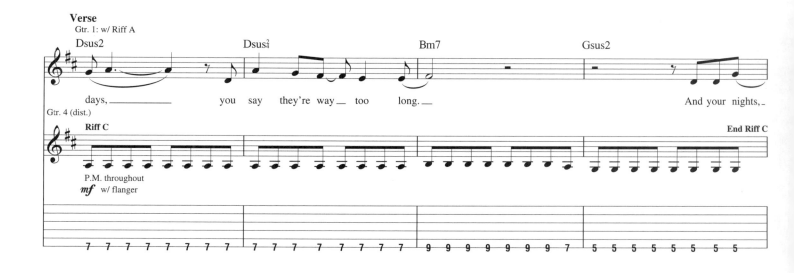

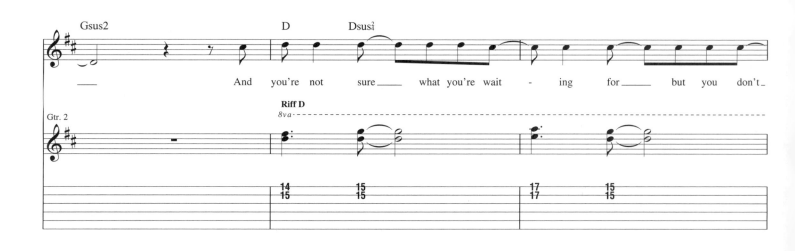

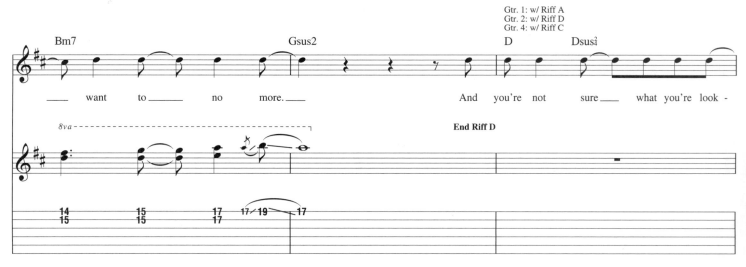

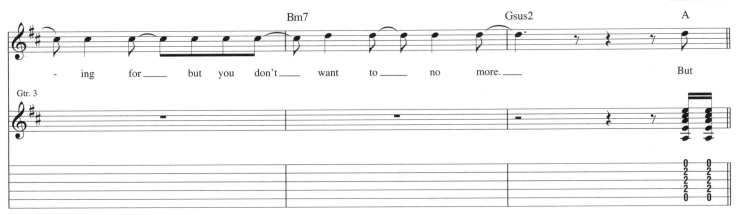

- ing for ___ but you don't ___ want to ___ no more. ___ But

⊕ Coda

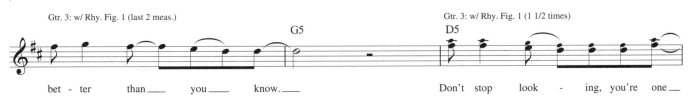

bet - ter than ___ you ___ know. ___ Don't stop look - ing, you're one

___ step clos - er. Don't stop search - ing, it's ___ not o - ver. Hold ___

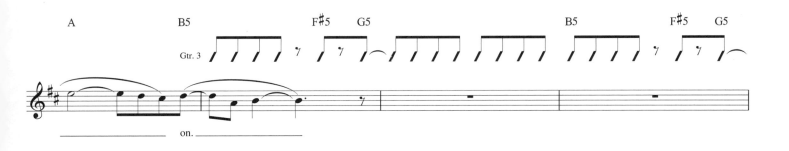

___ on. ___

Interlude

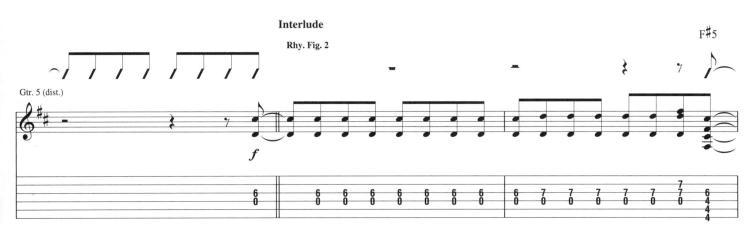

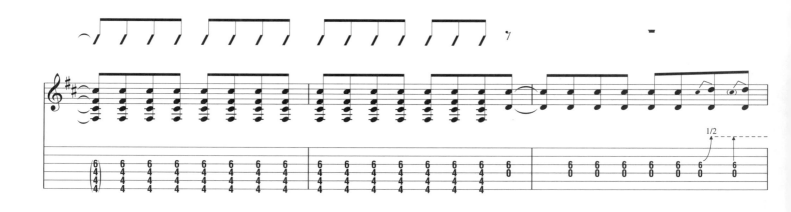

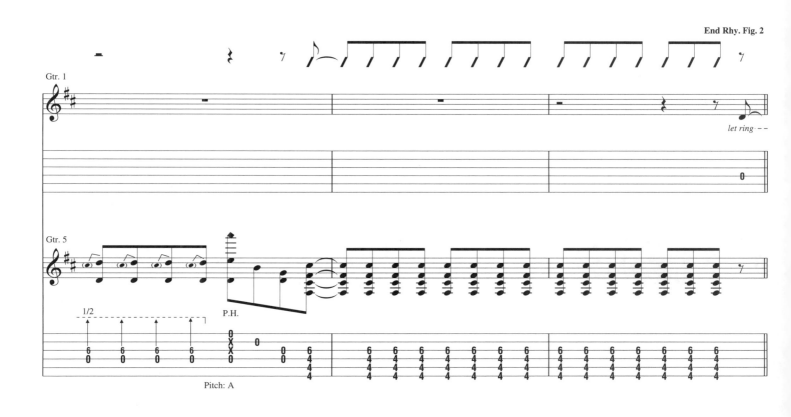

Bridge

Gtrs. 3 & 5: w/ Rhy. Fig. 2 (1st 4 meas.)

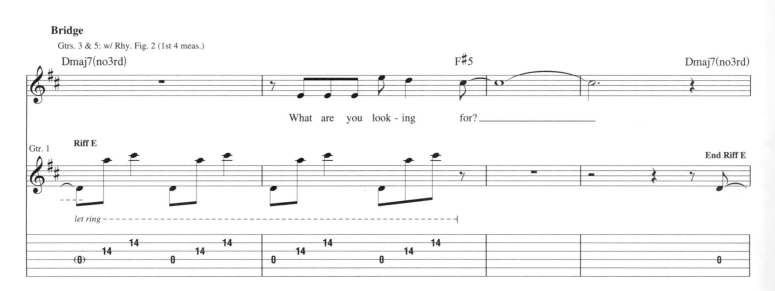

What are you look-ing for?

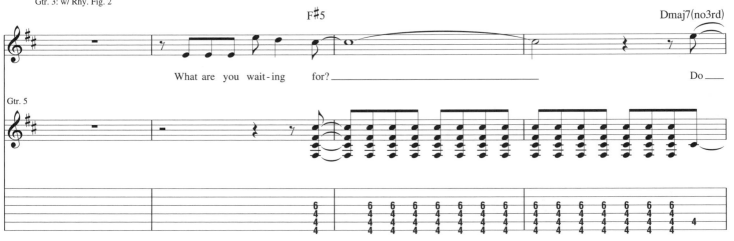

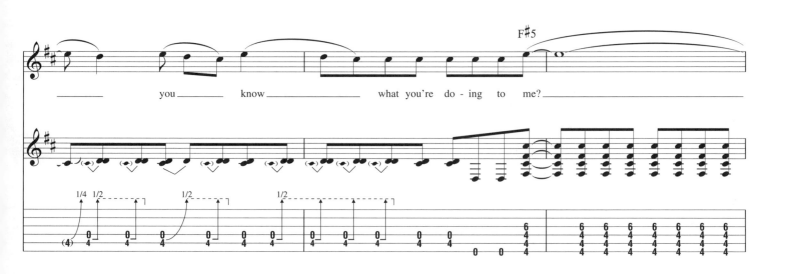

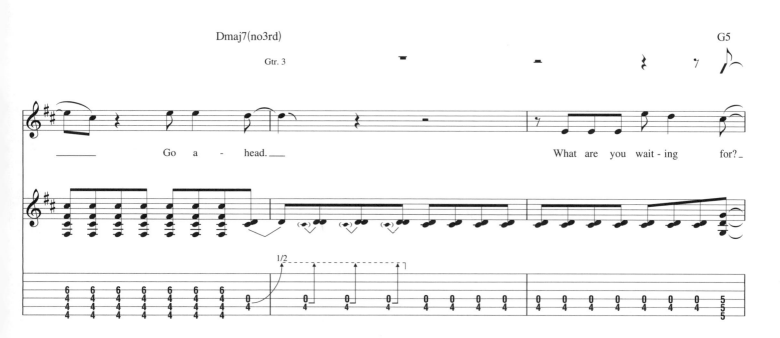

Chorus
Gtr. 3: w/ Rhy. Fig. 1 (2 1/2 times)
Gtr. 5 tacet

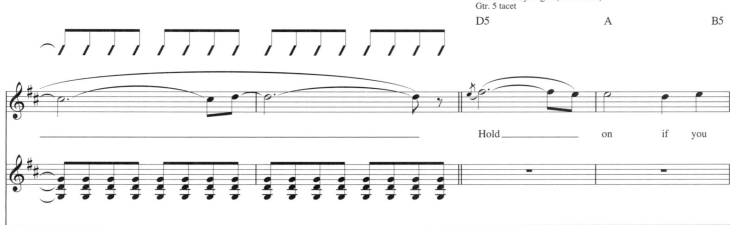

Hold _____ on if you

feel like let - ting ___ go. ___   Hold _____ on.   It gets

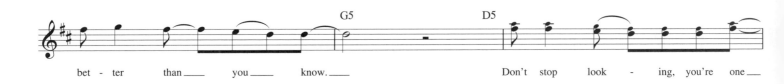

bet - ter than ___ you ___ know. ___   Don't stop look - ing, you're one ___

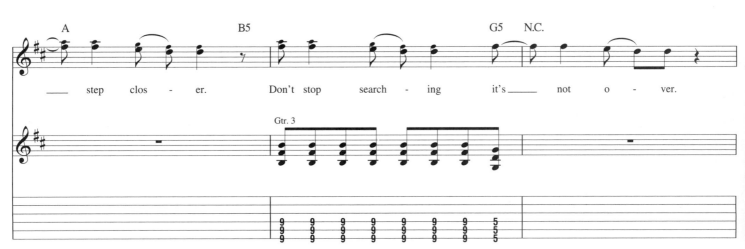

___ step clos - er.   Don't stop search - ing it's ___ not o - ver.

70

Gtr. 3: w/ Rhy. Fig. 1 (2 times)

Hold _____ on if you feel like let - ting ___ go. ___

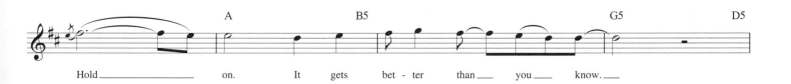

Hold _____ on. It gets bet - ter than ___ you ___ know. ___

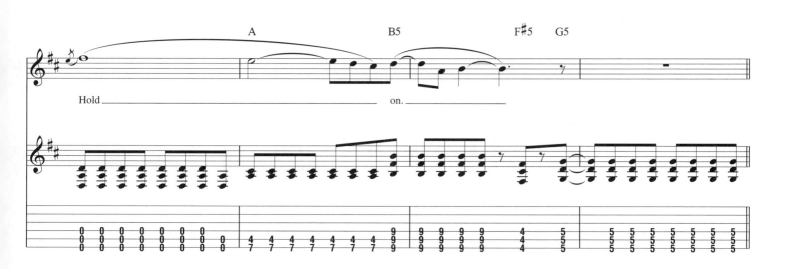

Hold _____ on. _____

Outro

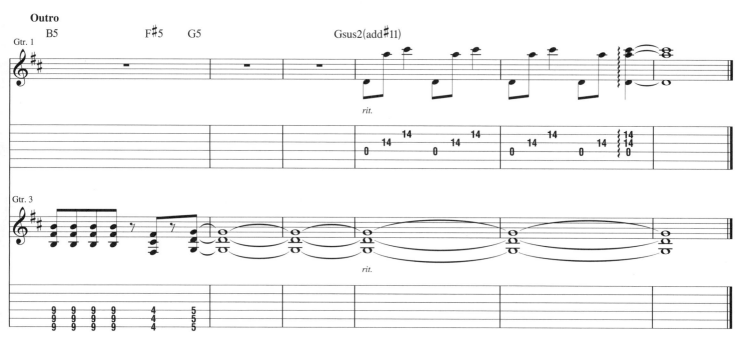

Riot Girl

Words and Music by Benjamin Combs and Joel Combs

Tune down 1/2 step:
(low to high) E♭-A♭-D♭-G♭-B♭-E♭

Intro
Fast Rock ♩ = 176

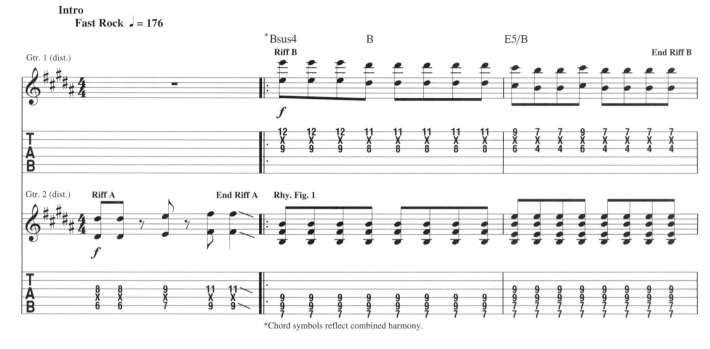

*Chord symbols reflect combined harmony.

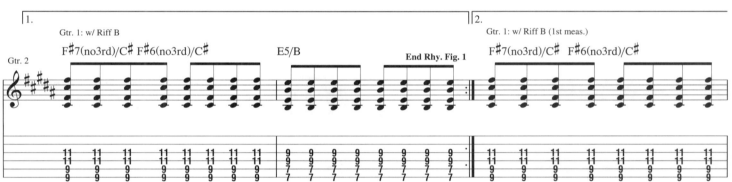

Verse

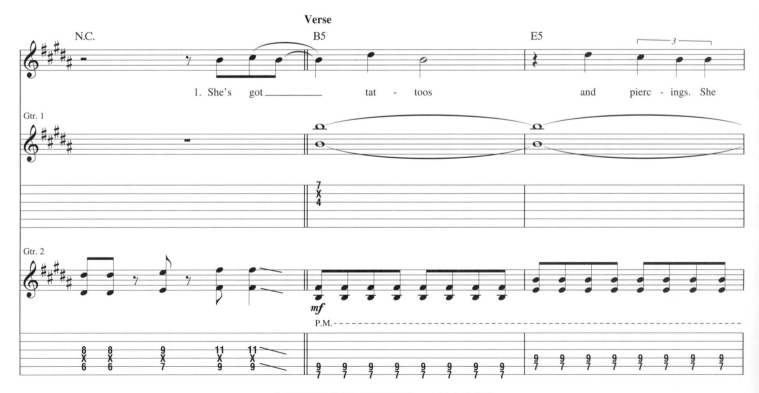

1. She's got tat-toos and pierc-ings. She

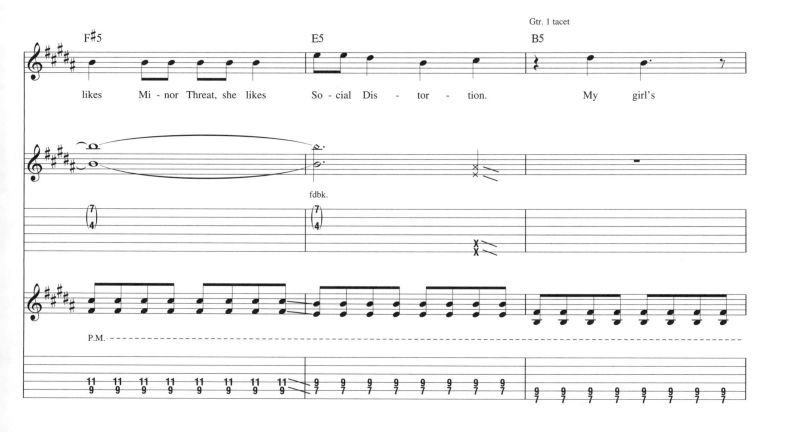

likes Mi - nor Threat, she likes So - cial Dis - tor - tion. My girl's

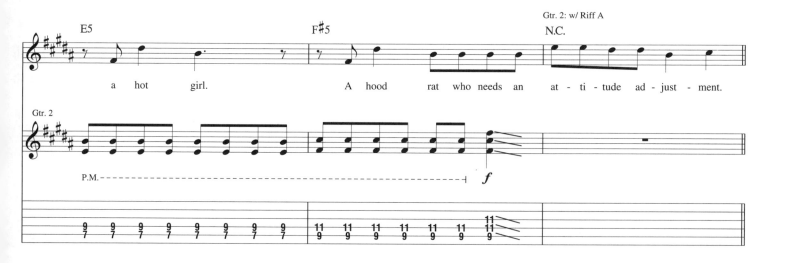

a hot girl. A hood rat who needs an at - ti - tude ad - just - ment.

Pre-Chorus

Gtr. 2: w/ Rhy. Fig. 1 (1 1/2 times)

Chris - ti - na would - n't wan - na meet her. She hates you Brit - ney, so you

bet - ter run for cov - er. My girl's a hot girl.

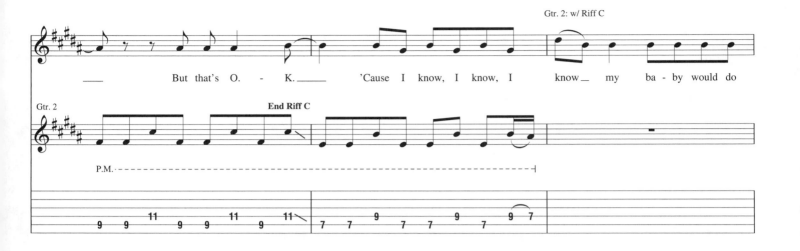

But that's O. - K. ___ 'Cause I know, I know, I know ___ my ba - by would do

an - y - thing ___ for ___ me. Yeah. ___

Pre-Chorus

___ Chris - ti - na would - n't wan - na meet her. She hates you Brit - ney, so you

bet - ter run for cov - er. My girl's a hot girl.

D.S. al Coda 1

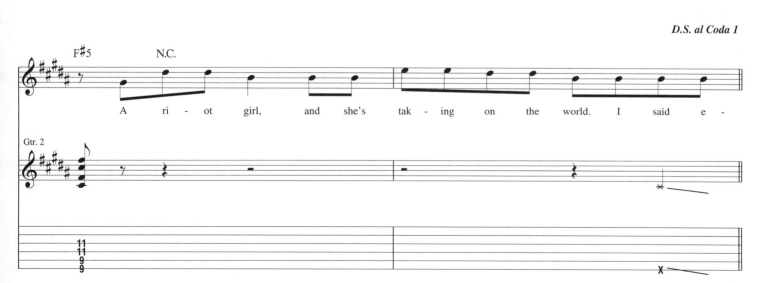

A ri - ot girl, and she's tak - ing on the world. I said e -

Coda 1

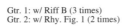

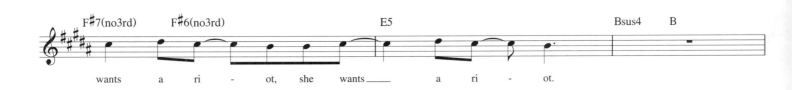

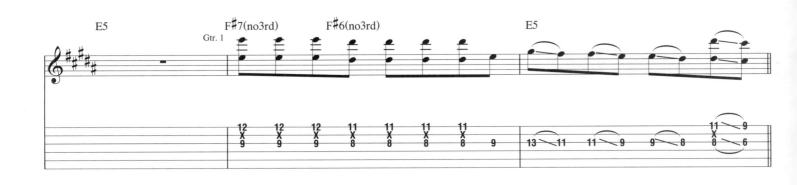

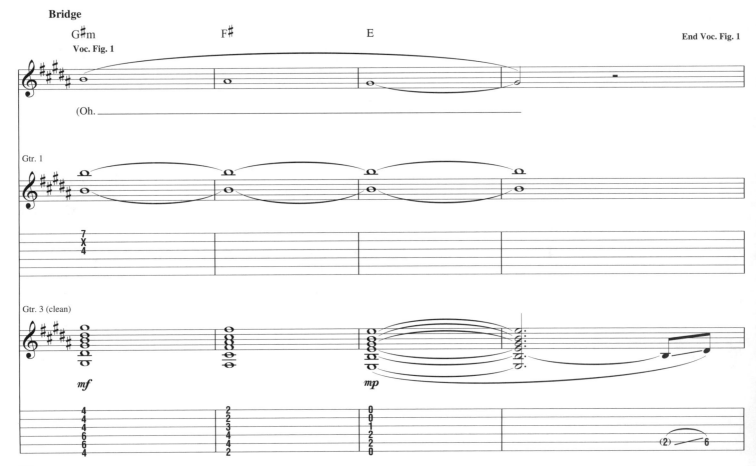

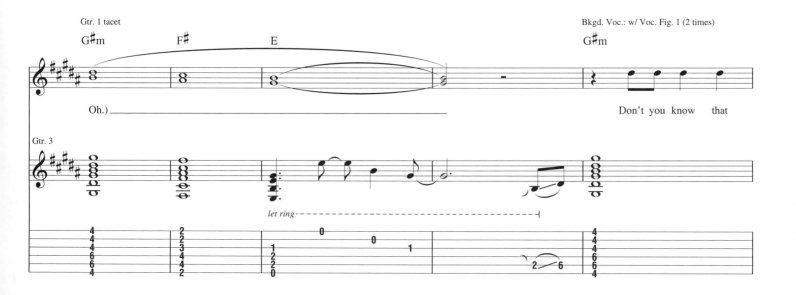

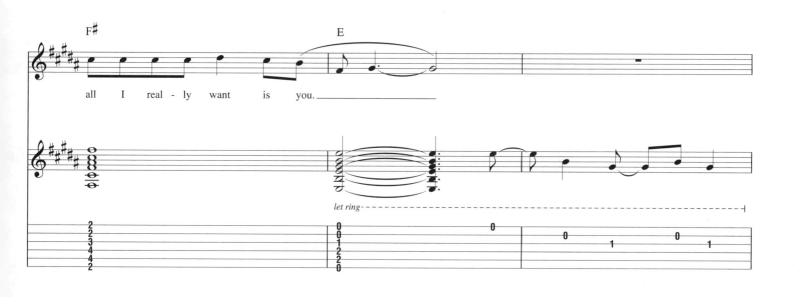

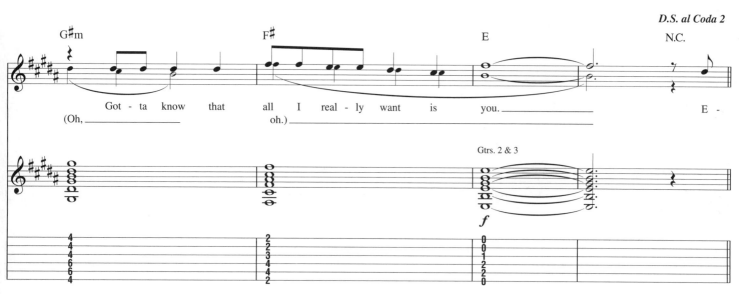

✪ Coda 2

Outro

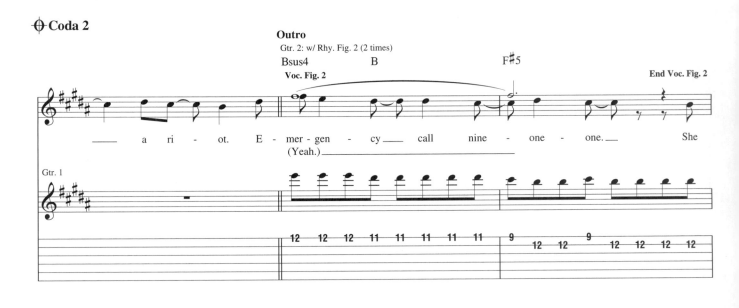

a ri - ot. E - mer - gen - cy __ call nine - one - one. __ She
(Yeah.) _____

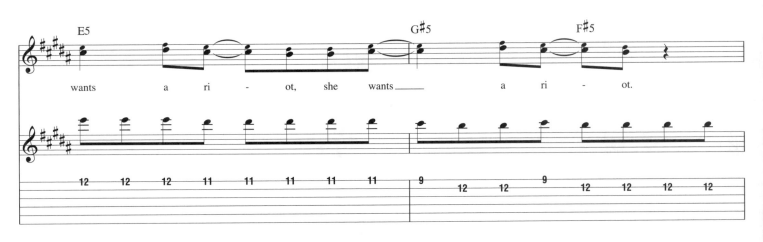

wants a ri - ot, she wants _____ a ri - ot.

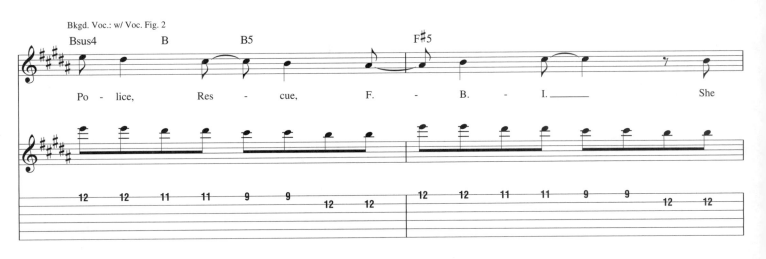

Po - lice, Res - cue, F. - B. - I. _____ She

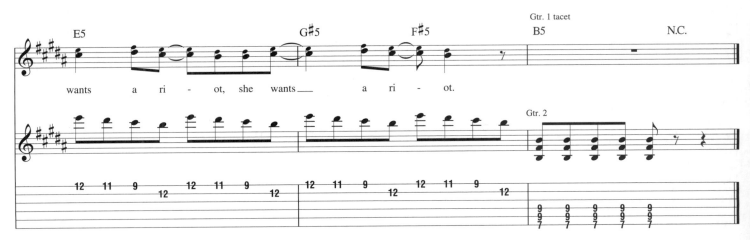

wants a ri - ot, she wants _____ a ri - ot.

Say Anything

Words and Music by Benjamin Combs and Joel Combs

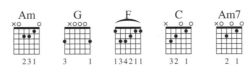

Gtrs. 1 & 4: Tune down 1/2 step:
(low to high) Bb-Eb-Ab-Db-Gb-Bb-Eb
Gtrs. 2, 3 & 5: Tune down 1/2 step:
(low to high) Eb-Ab-Db-Gb-Bb-Eb

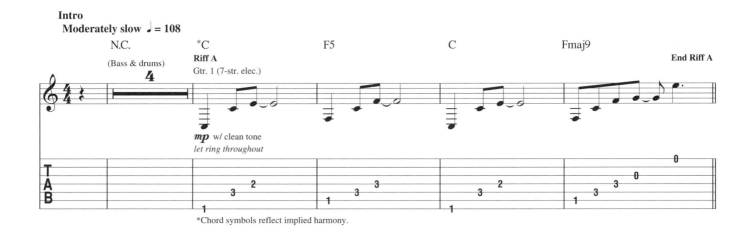

*Chord symbols reflect implied harmony.

Verse

Gtr. 1: w/ Riff A (3 times)

1. Here I am on the phone a - gain and

awk - ward si - lenc - es on the oth - er end.

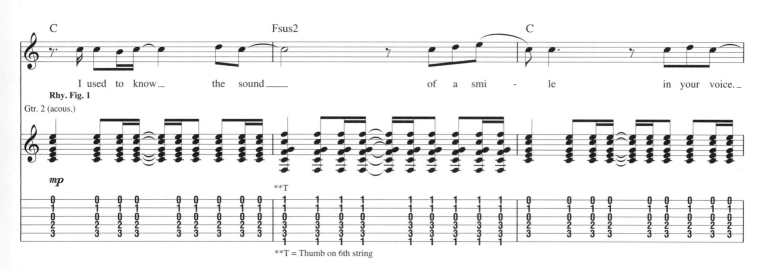

I used to know the sound of a smi - le in your voice.

**T = Thumb on 6th string

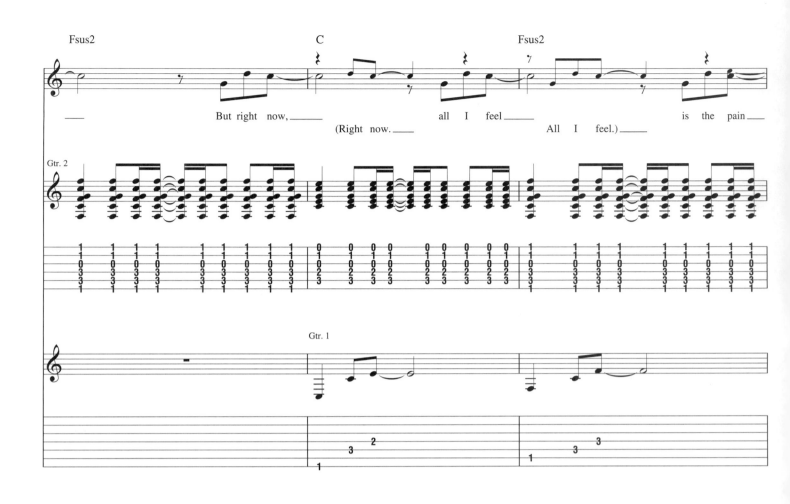

But right now,_____   all I feel_____   is the pain_____
(Right now._____   All I feel.)_____

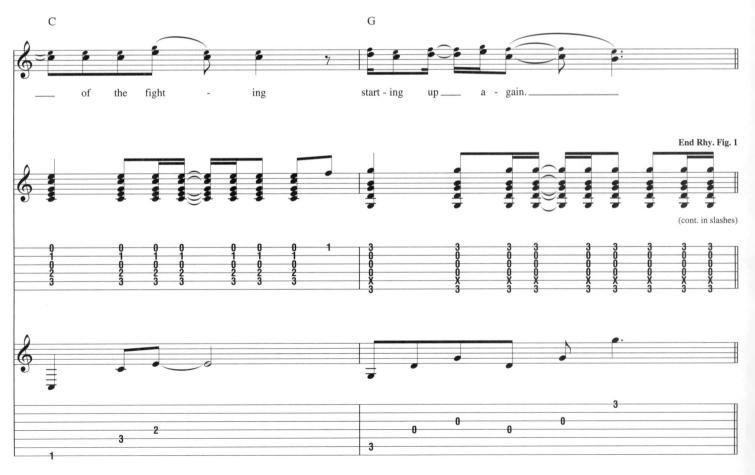

_____ of the fight - ing   start - ing up_____ a - gain._____

End Rhy. Fig. 1

(cont. in slashes)

All the things___ we talk___ a - bout,___ you know, they___ stay on my mind,___

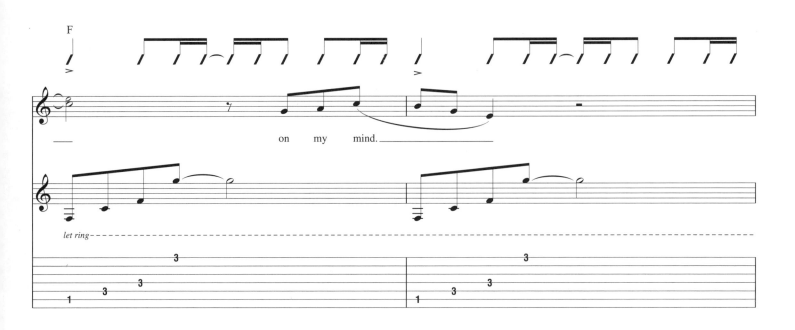

___ on my mind.___

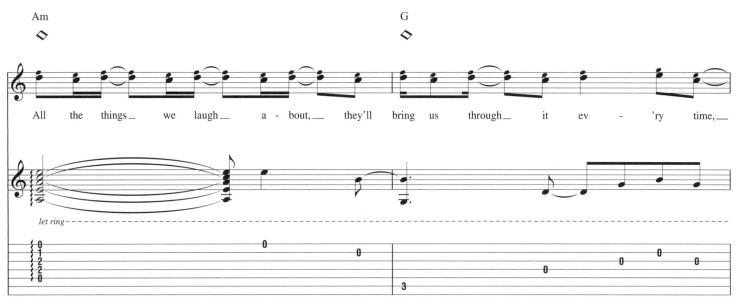

All the things___ we laugh___ a - bout,___ they'll bring us through___ it ev - 'ry time,___

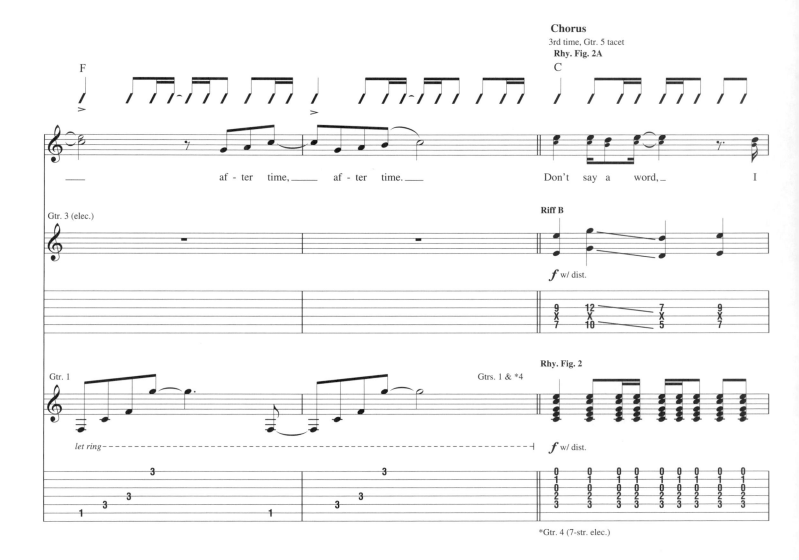

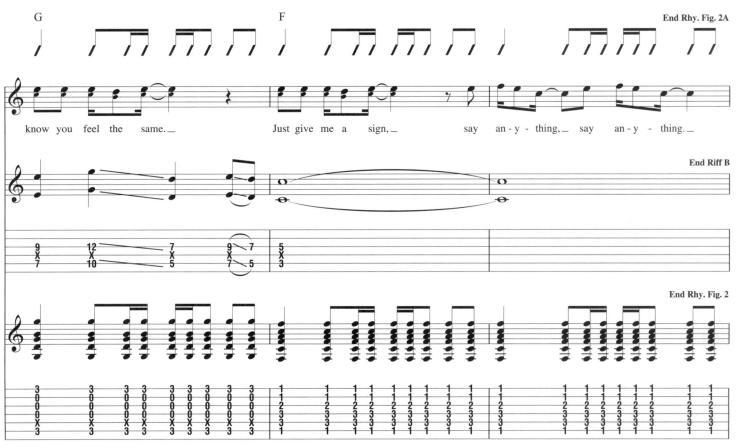

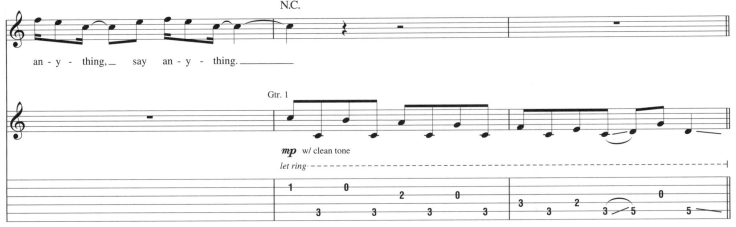

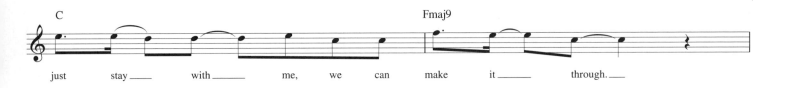

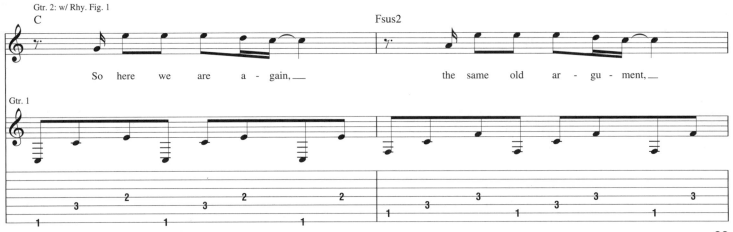

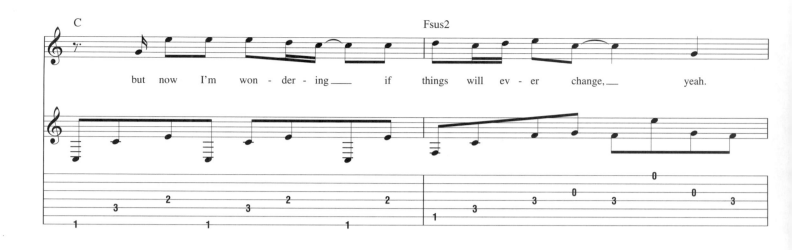

but now I'm won-der-ing ___ if things will ev - er change, ___ yeah.

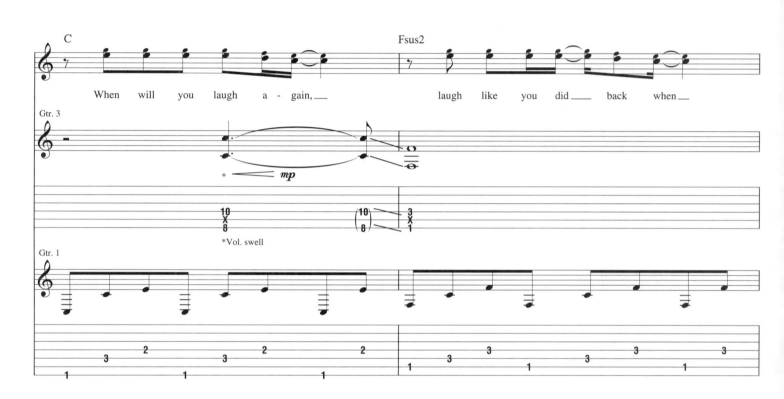

When will you laugh a - gain, ___ laugh like you did ___ back when ___

*Vol. swell

D.S. al Coda 1

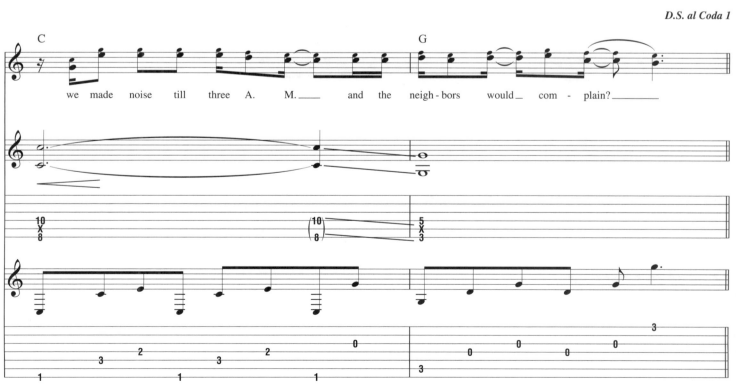

we made noise till three A. M. ___ and the neigh-bors would ___ com - plain? ___

✆ Coda 1

*Chord symbols reflect overall harmony.

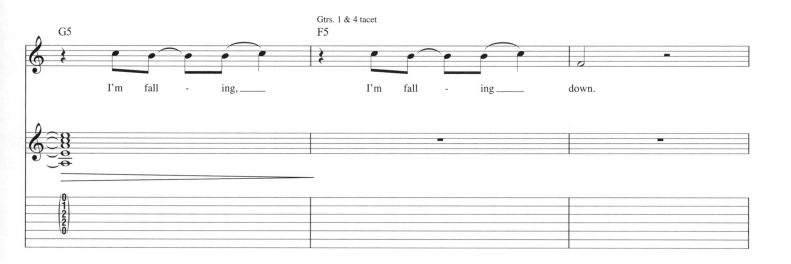

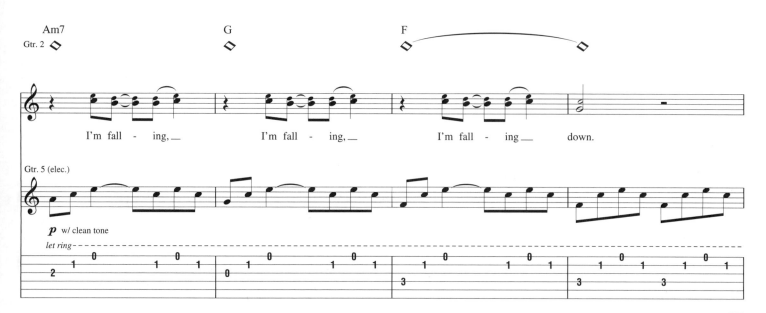

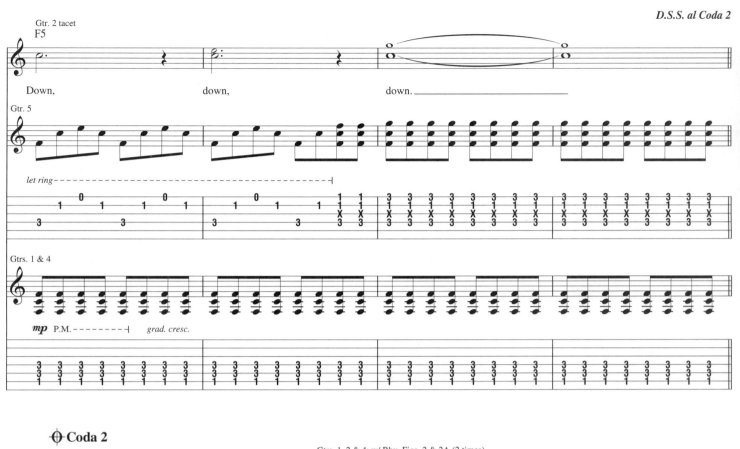

Gtr. 2 tacet

F5

Down, down, down.

Gtr. 5

let ring

Gtrs. 1 & 4

mp P.M. *grad. cresc.*

Coda 2

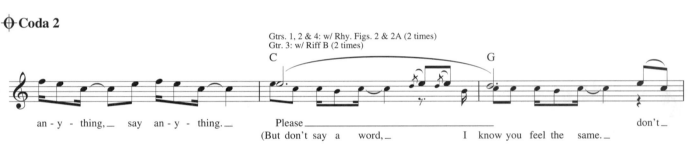

Gtrs. 1, 2 & 4: w/ Rhy. Figs. 2 & 2A (2 times)
Gtr. 3: w/ Riff B (2 times)

C   G

an - y - thing,__ say an - y - thing.__   Please_____   don't
(But don't say a word,__   I know you feel the same.__

F   C

leave.   Say an - y - thing,__ say an - y - thing.__   Please_____
Just give me a sign.__   Don't walk a - way,__   I

G   F

__   don't__ leave.   Say an - y - thing,__ say an - y - thing.__
know you wan - na stay.__   Just give me a sign.)__

N.C.   C

Gtrs. 1 & 4

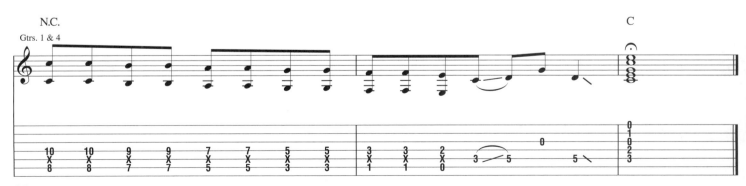

The Day That I Die

Words and Music by Benjamin Combs and Joel Combs

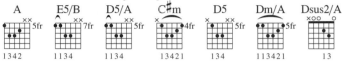

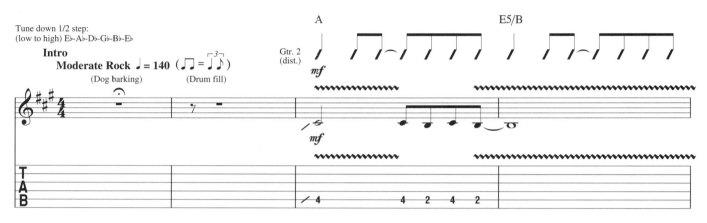

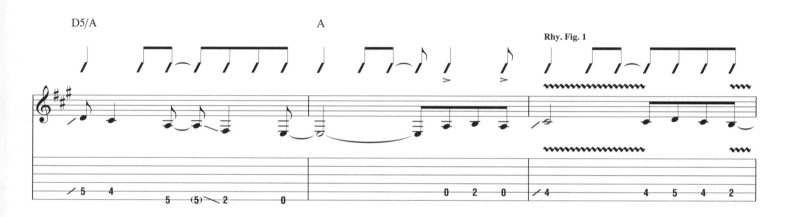

1. One day I woke up, I woke up know-ing to-day is the day ___ I will die. ___

Cash - dogg was bark - ing, went to the park and en -

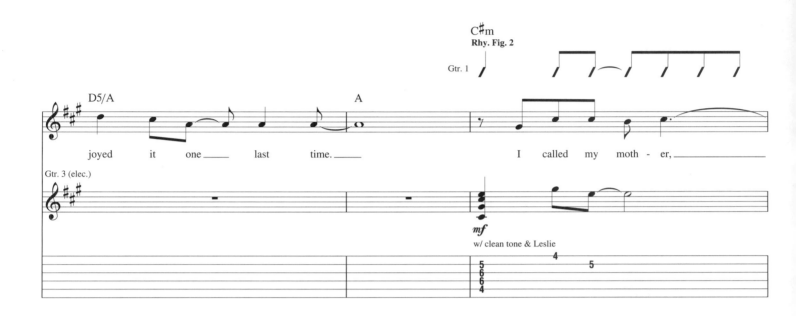

joyed it one ___ last time. ___ I called my moth - er, ___

Gtr. 3 (elec.)

mf

w/ clean tone & Leslie

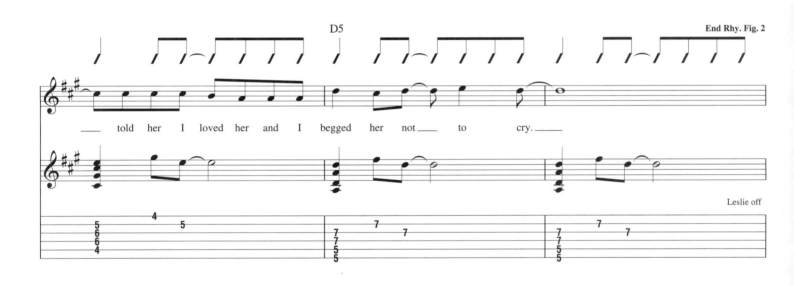

___ told her I loved her and I begged her not ___ to cry. ___

Leslie off

Gtr. 1: w/ Rhy. Fig. 1

*A

Esus2

Dsus2/A

I wrote a let - ter ___ that said I'd miss her, and I signed that ___ good - bye...

Rhy. Fig. 3

w/ dist.

let ring --------

let ring --------

*Chord symbols reflect basic harmony.

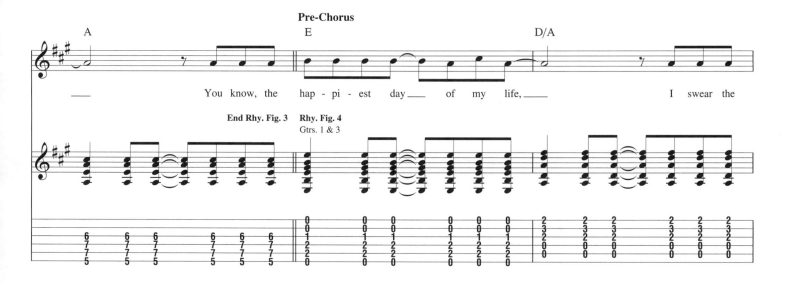

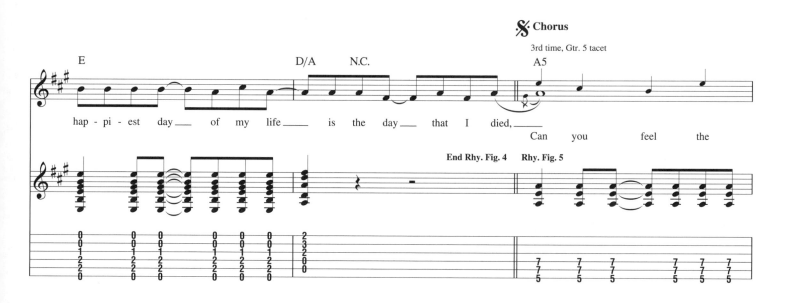

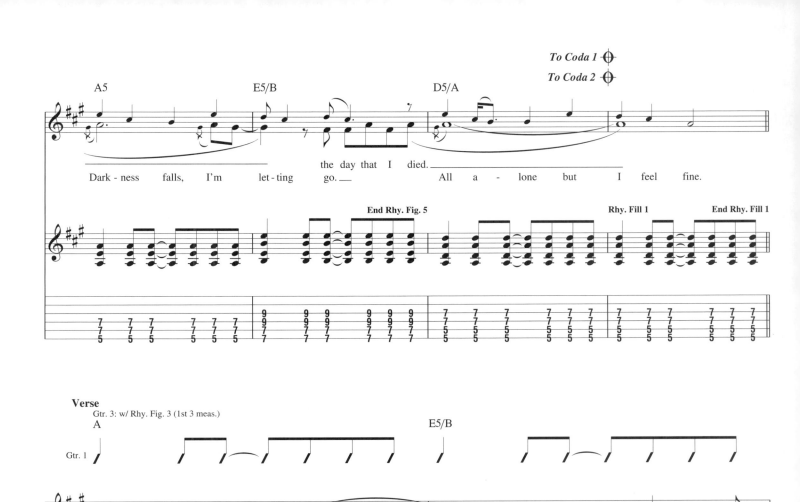

Dark - ness falls, I'm let - ting go. ___ the day that I died. ___ All a - lone but I feel fine.

End Rhy. Fig. 5   Rhy. Fill 1   End Rhy. Fill 1

Verse
Gtr. 3: w/ Rhy. Fig. 3 (1st 3 meas.)

2. We took a drive and ___ we drove through D. C. to

see the plac - es we lived. ___ Long con - ver - sa - tions,

Gtrs. 1 & 3: w/ Rhy. Figs. 1 & 3

Gtr. 4 (dist.)

Gtr. 4 tacet

___ we talked of old friends and all the things ___ that we did.

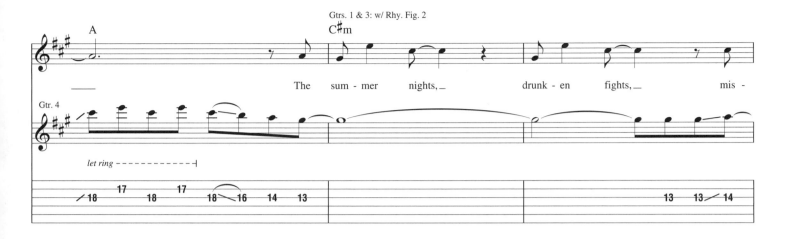

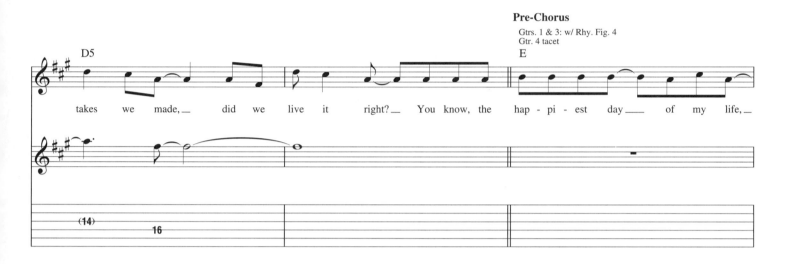

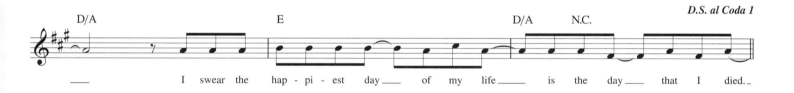

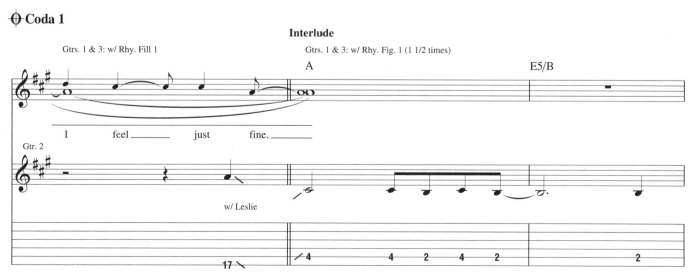

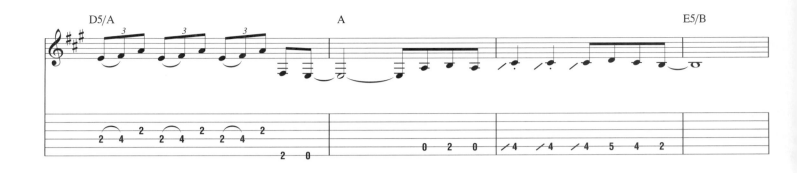

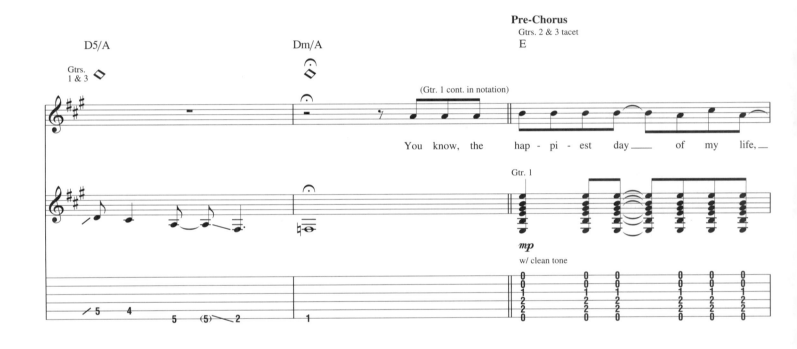

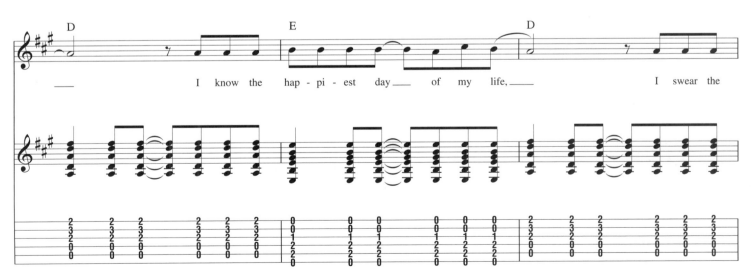

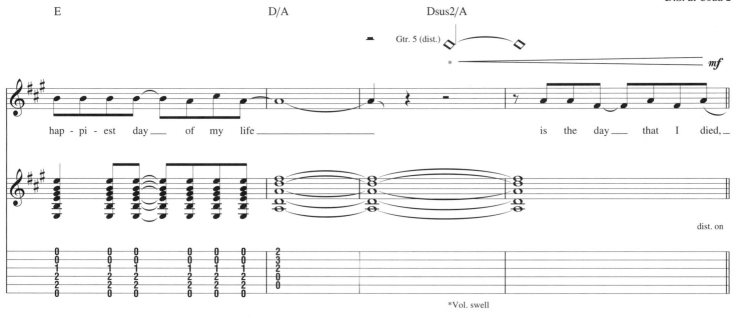

Coda 2

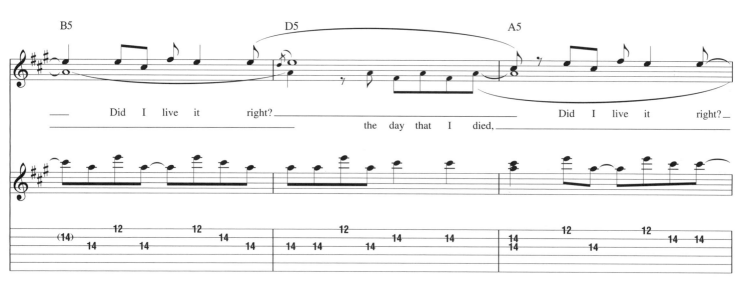

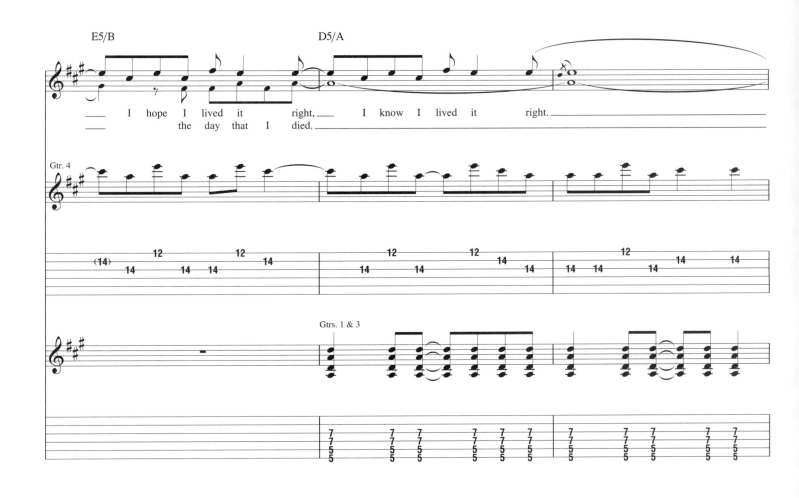

I hope I lived it right, ___ I know I lived it right. ___
the day that I died. ___

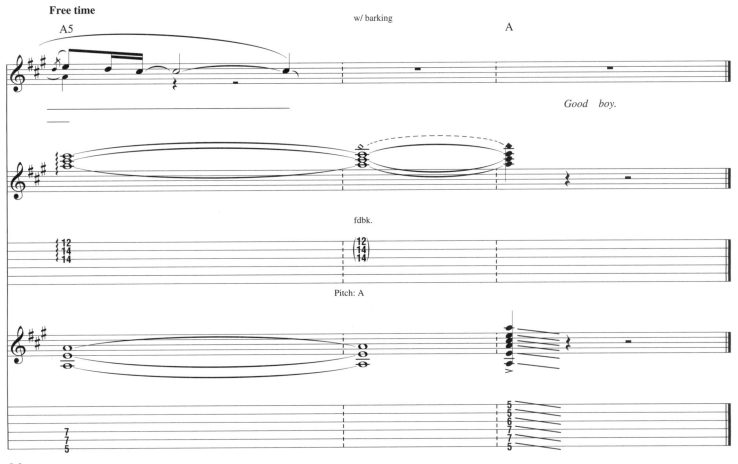

Free time

w/ barking

Good boy.

fdbk.

Pitch: A

The Young & The Hopeless

Words and Music by Benjamin Combs and Joel Combs

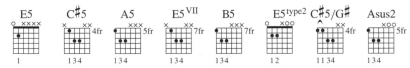

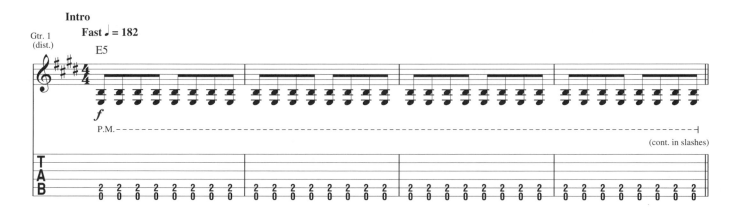

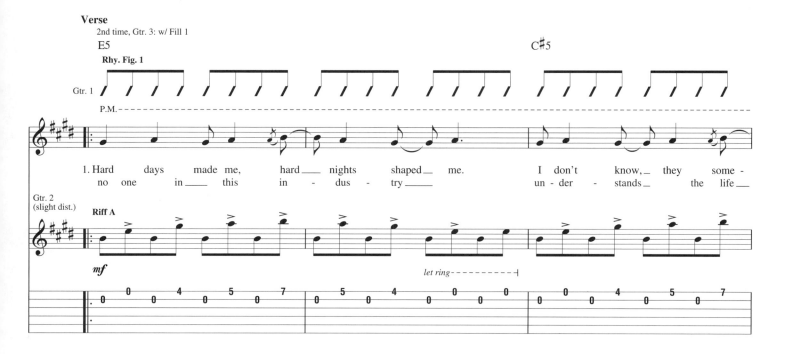

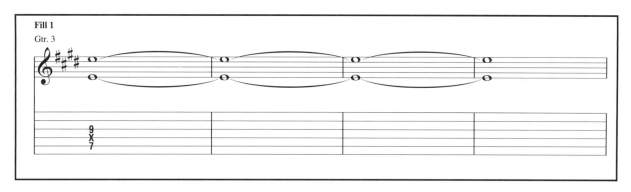

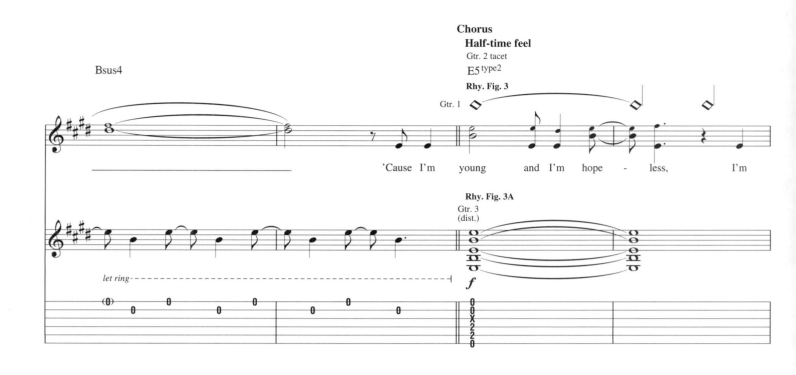

Chorus
Half-time feel
Gtr. 2 tacet
E5 type2
Rhy. Fig. 3
Gtr. 1

Bsus4

'Cause I'm young and I'm hope - less, I'm

Rhy. Fig. 3A
Gtr. 3
(dist.)

let ring

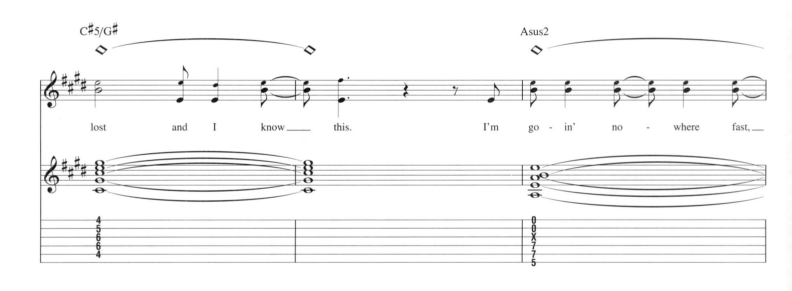

C#5/G#

Asus2

lost and I know this. I'm go - in' no - where fast,

End half-time feel
B5

End Rhy. Fig. 3

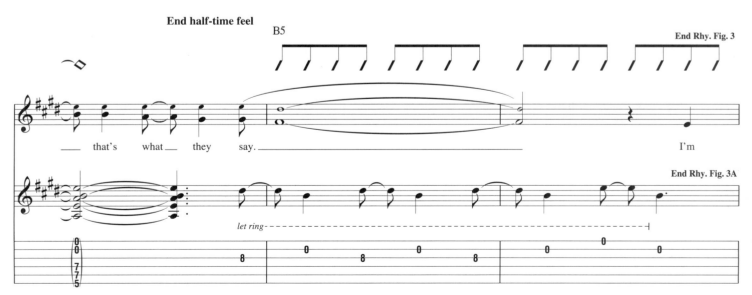

that's what they say.

I'm

End Rhy. Fig. 3A

let ring

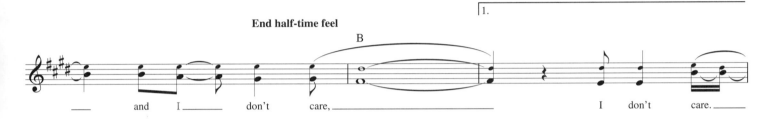

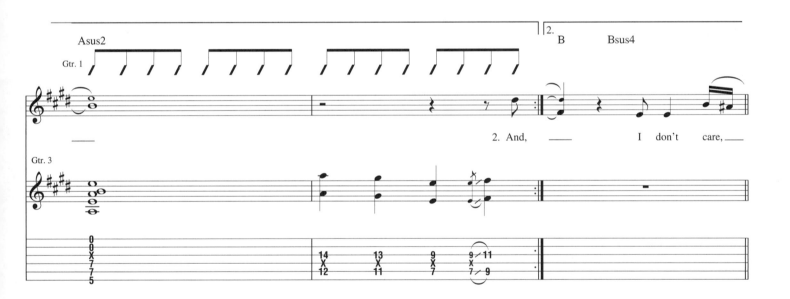

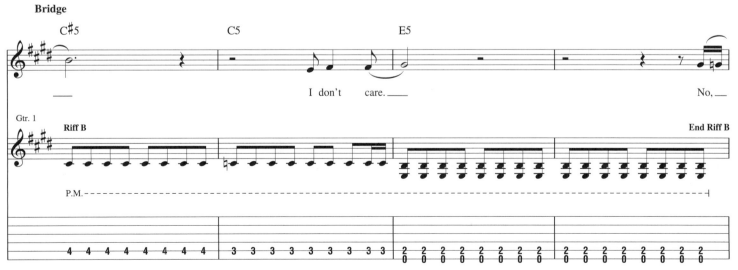

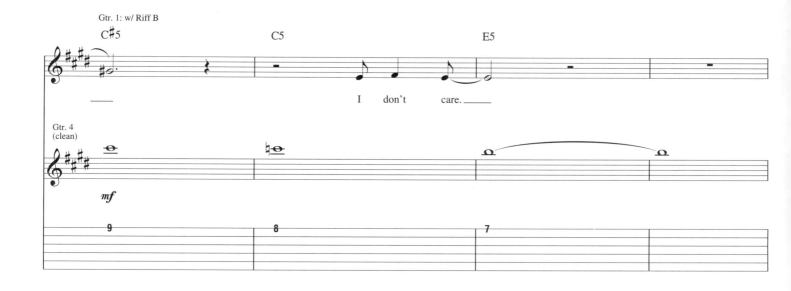

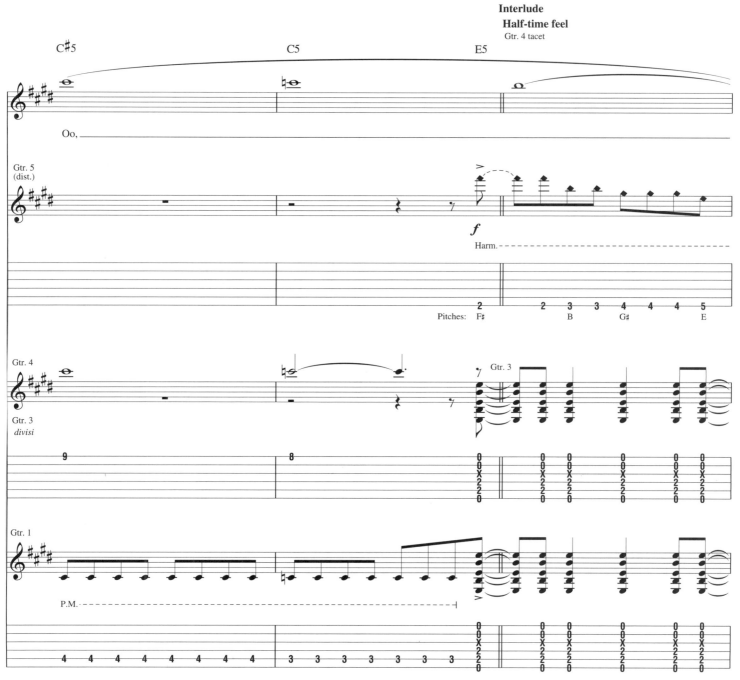

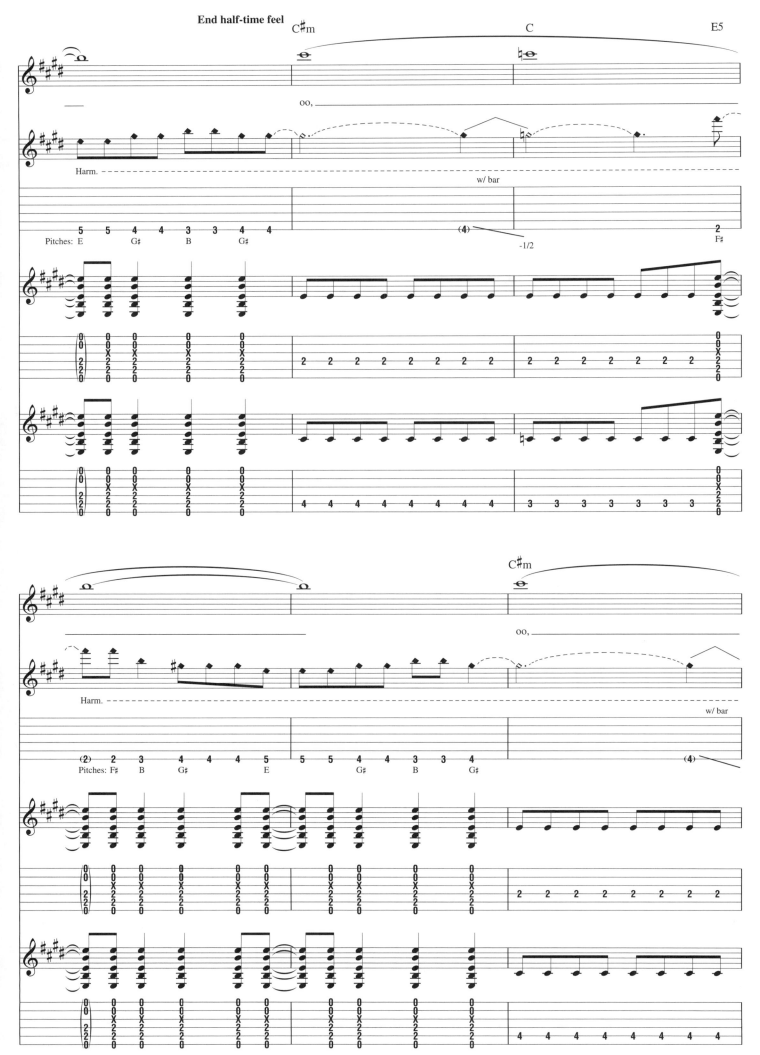

Chorus

Gtrs. 1 & 3: w/ Rhy. Figs. 3 & 3A (2 times)

Gtr. 5 tacet

young and I'm hope - less, I'm lost and I know ___

___ this. I'm go - in' no - where fast, ___ that's what ___ they say.

And I'm trou - ble - some, ___ I'm fall -

- en, I'm an - gry at ___ my fa - ther, it's

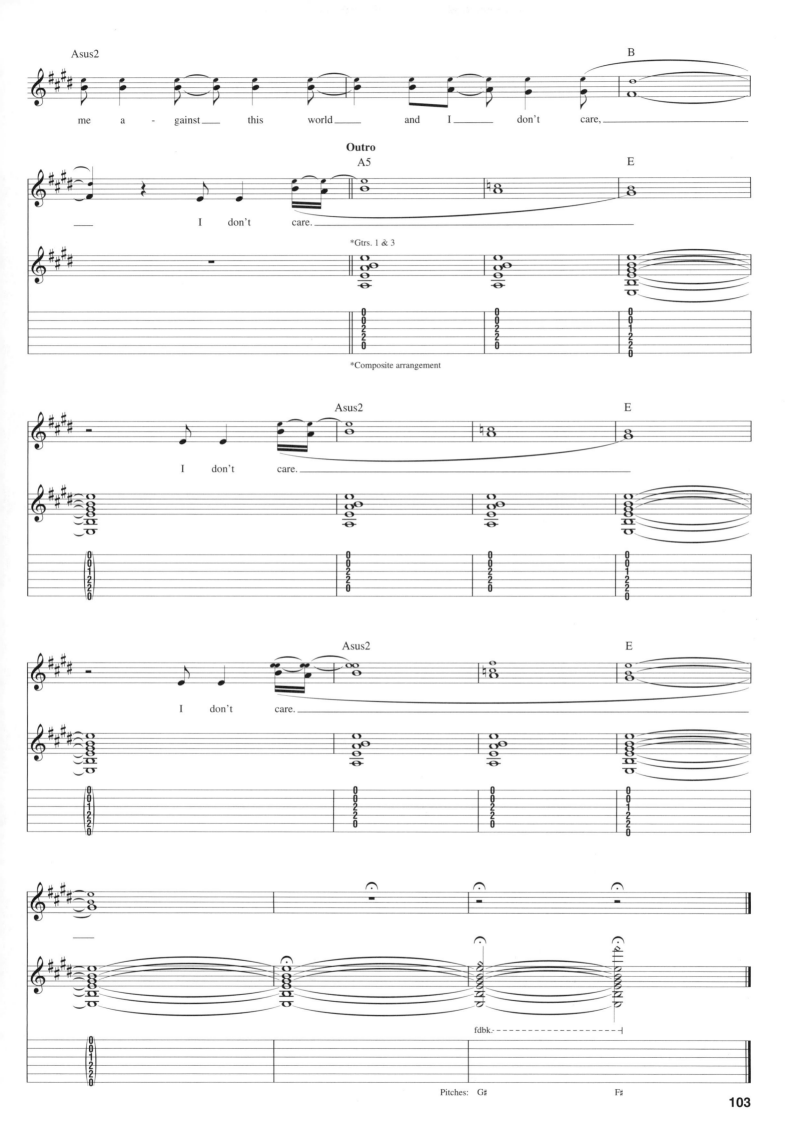

Emotionless

Words and Music by Benjamin Combs and Joel Combs

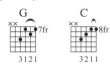

Tune down 1/2 step:
(low to high) Eb-Ab-Db-Gb-Bb-Eb

Verse

Moderately slow ♩ = 74

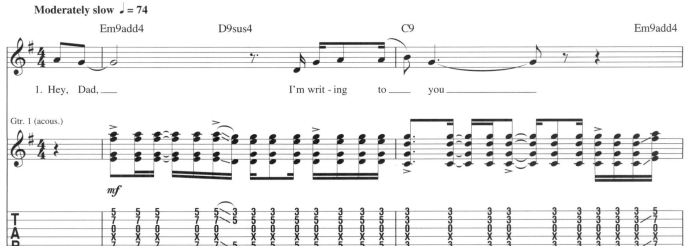

1. Hey, Dad, ___ I'm writ-ing to ___ you ___

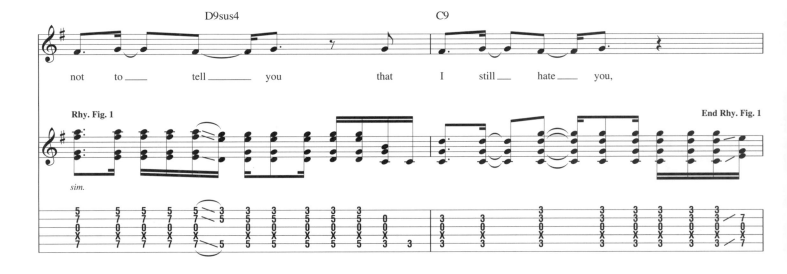

not to ___ tell ___ you that I still ___ hate ___ you,

just to ___ ask ___ you how you feel, ___ and how we

fell a - part,_____ how this fell a - part._____ Are you

Gtr. 1: w/ Rhy. Fig. 1 (3 1/2 times)

Em9add4   D9sus4   C9   Em9add4

hap - py____ out____ there in this great wide__ world?____ Do you

D9sus4   C9   Em9add4

think a - bout__ your sons?____ Do you miss your lit - tle girl?____ When you

D9sus4   C9   Em9add4

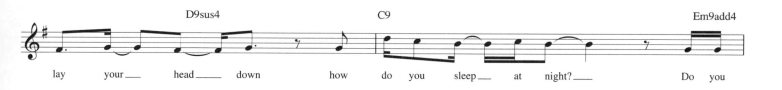

lay your__ head__ down how do you sleep__ at night?____ Do you

Gtr. 1: w/ Rhy. Fig. 2 (3 times)

D9sus4   C9

e - ven__ won - der if we're al - right?____ We're al -

right. _____ We're al - right. _____ It's been a

Chorus

long, hard road with-out___ you by my side. Why weren't you there all the nights___ that we cried? You

broke my moth-er's heart, you broke your chil-dren for life.___ It's not O. K.___ but we're al-right. I re-

mem-ber the days___ you were a he-ro in my eyes, but those are just a long lost mem-'ry of mine.___ I spent

so man-y years___ learn-ing how to sur-vive.___ Now I'm writ-ing just to let you know we're still a - live.___

2. The days I___ spent___ so

cold, so___ hun - gry were full of___ hate.___ I

was so___ an - gry. The scars run___ deep___ in - side this

tat - tooed___ bod - y. There's things I'll___ take to my___ grave.___

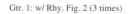
Gtr. 1: w/ Rhy. Fig. 2 (3 times)

But I'm O. K._____ I'm O. K.____

Chorus

Gtrs. 1 & 2: w/ Rhy. Figs. 3 & 3A

_____ It's been a long hard road with-out____ you by my side.

Why weren't you there all the nights__ that we cried? You broke my moth-er's heart, you broke your chil-dren for life.__ It's

not O. K.____ but we're al - right.__ I re-mem-ber the days__ you were a he-ro in my eyes, but

those are just a long, lost mem-'ry of mine.__ Now I'm writ-ing just to let you know I'm still a-live.__ Yeah, I'm

Bridge

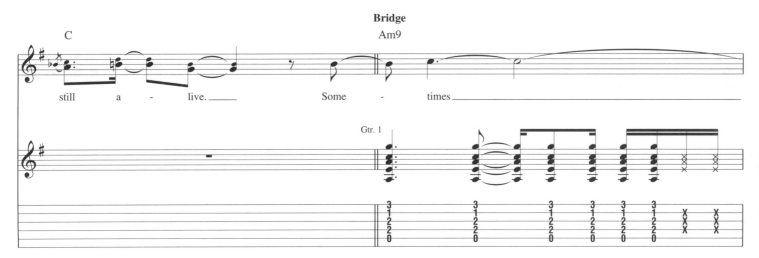

still a - live.____ Some - times____

Gtr. 1

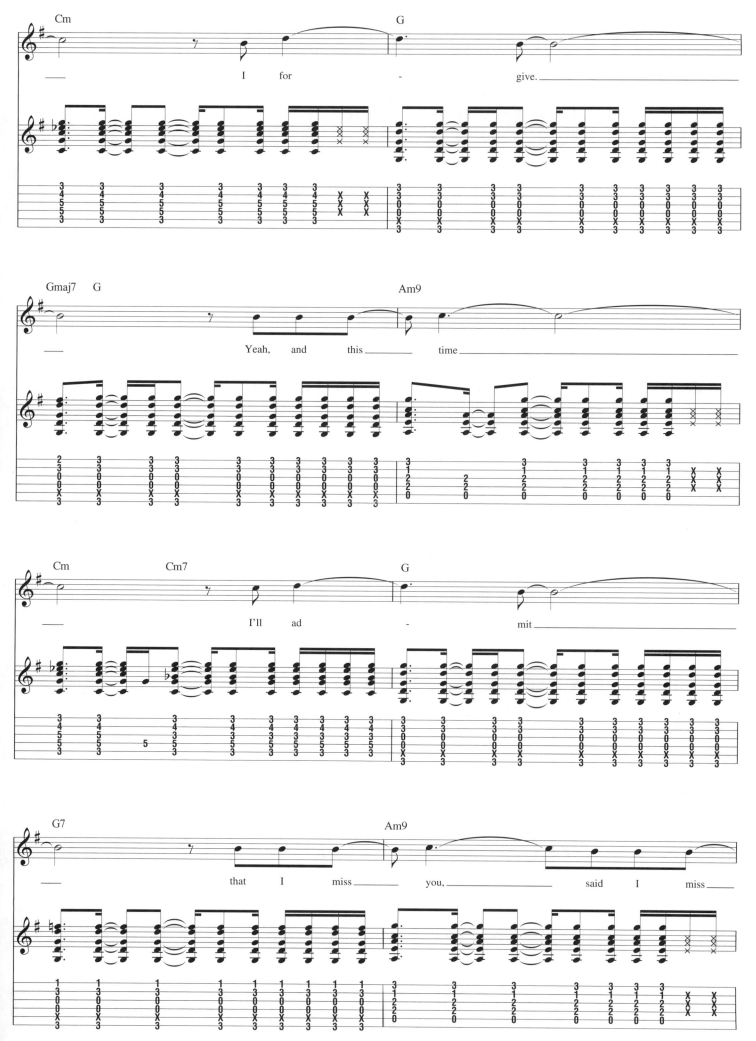

you. It's been a

Chorus

Gtrs. 1 & 2: w/ Rhy. Figs. 3 & 3A (1st 7 meas.)

long hard road with-out __ you by my side. Why weren't you there all the nights __ that we cried? You

broke my moth-er's heart, you broke your chil-dren for life. __ It's not O. K. __ but we're al - right. __ I re -

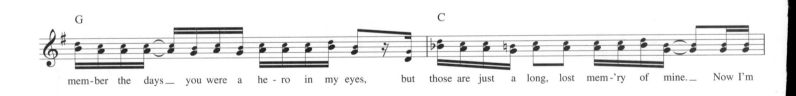

mem-ber the days __ you were a he - ro in my eyes, but those are just a long, lost mem-'ry of mine. __ Now I'm

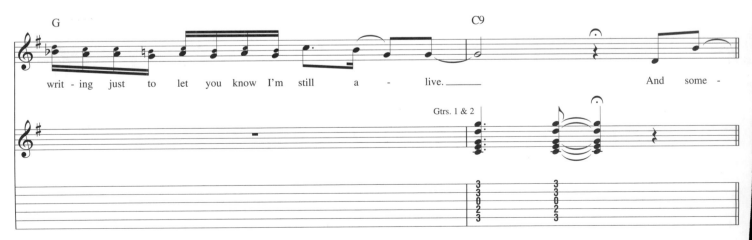

writ - ing just to let you know I'm still a - live. _____ And some -

Gtrs. 1 & 2

110

Movin' On

Words and Music by Benjamin Combs and Joel Combs

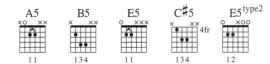

A5   B5   E5   C#5   E5 type2

Tune down 1/2 step:
(low to high) Eb-Ab-Db-Gb-Bb-Eb

Intro
Fast ♩ = 180

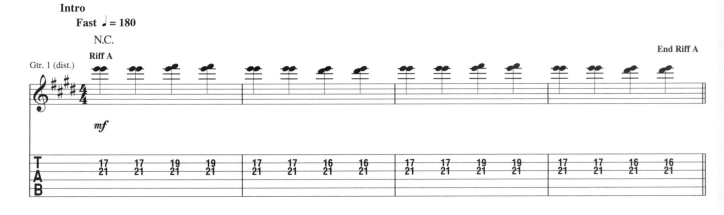

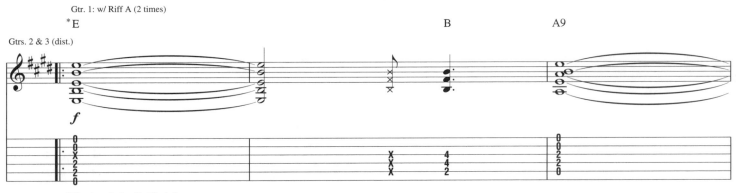

*Chord symbols reflect basic harmony.

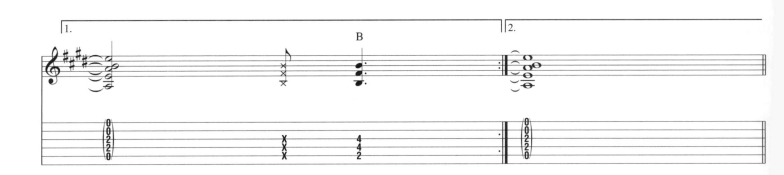

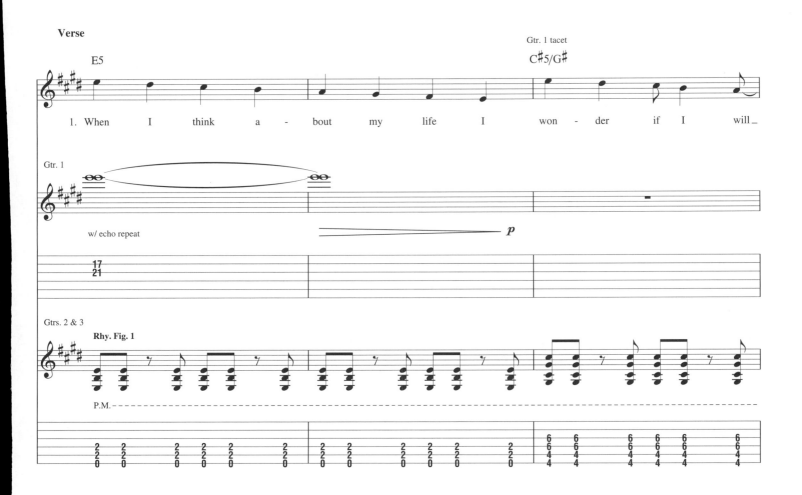

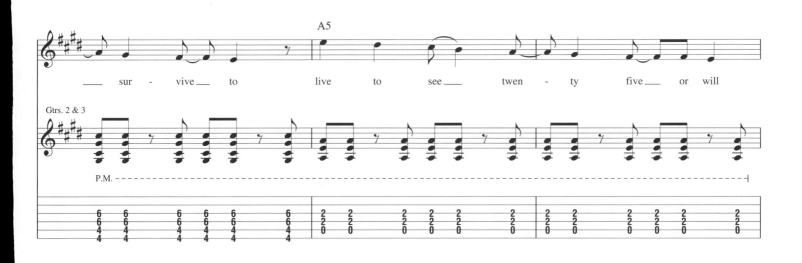

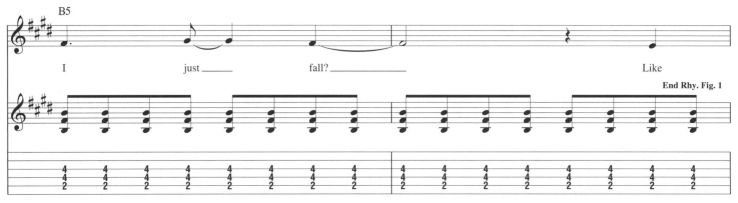

all my friends___ they just___ keep dy - ing. Peo - ple 'round___ me al -

- ways cry - ing in this place_____ that I_____

_____ like___ to call my_____ home._____ Well, not

Bridge

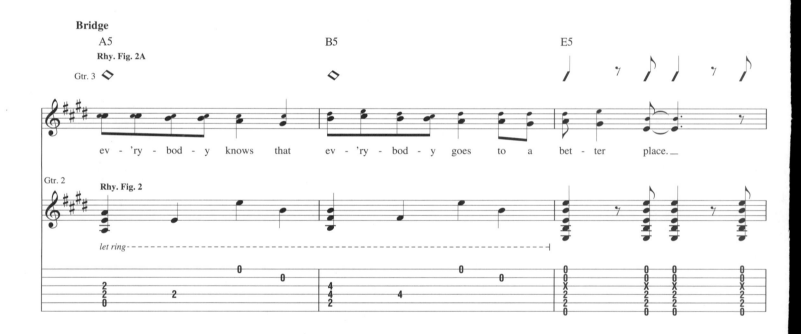

ev - 'ry - bod - y knows that ev - 'ry - bod - y goes to a bet - ter place.___

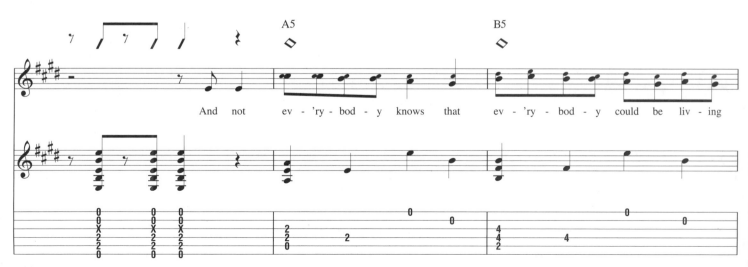

And not ev - 'ry - bod - y knows that ev - 'ry - bod - y could be liv - ing

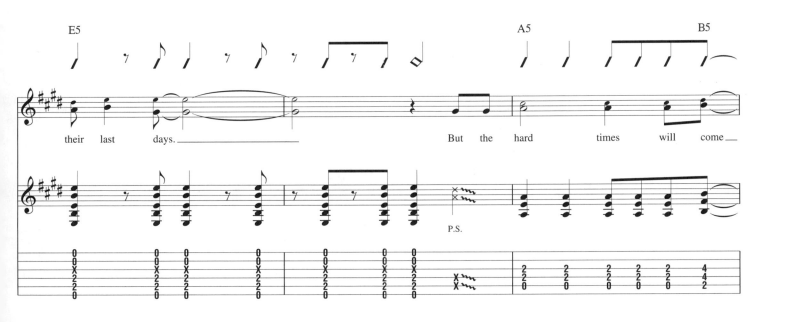

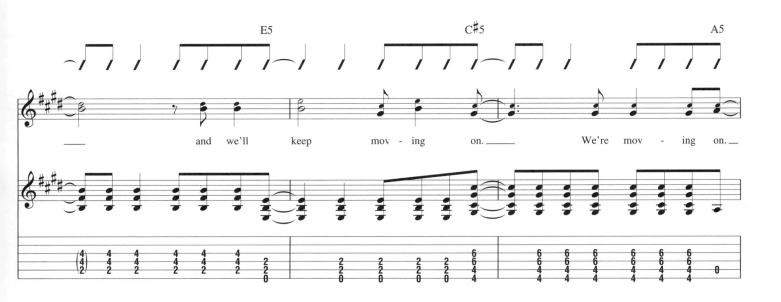

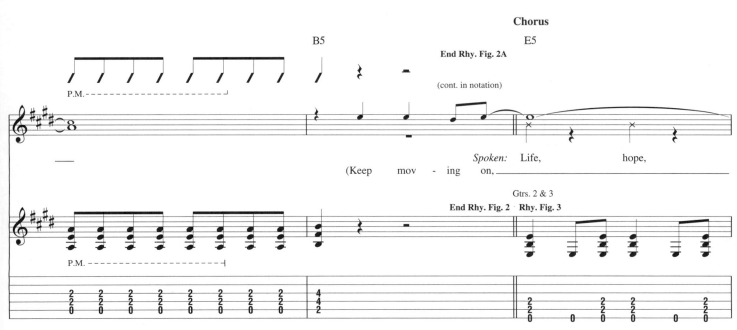

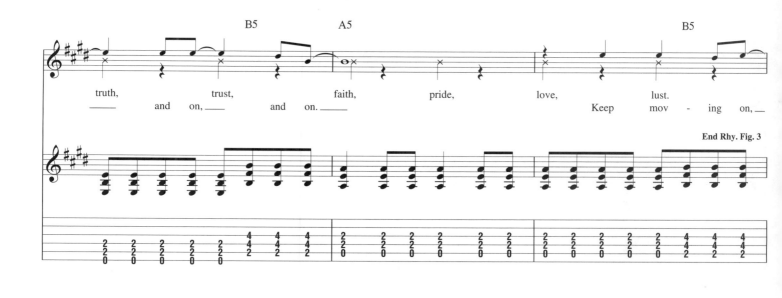

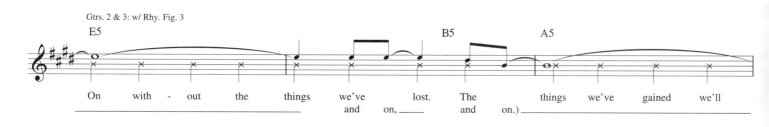

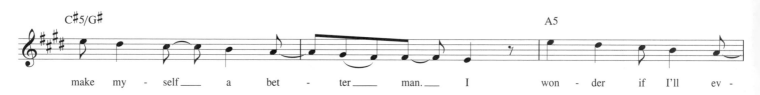

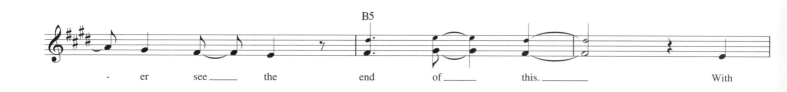

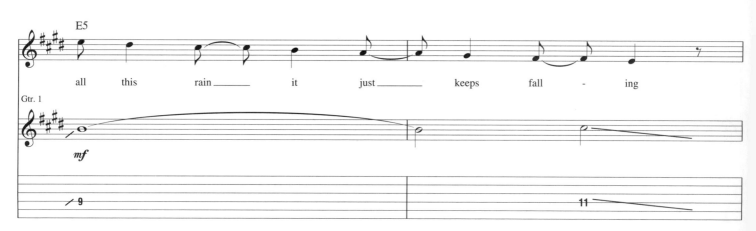

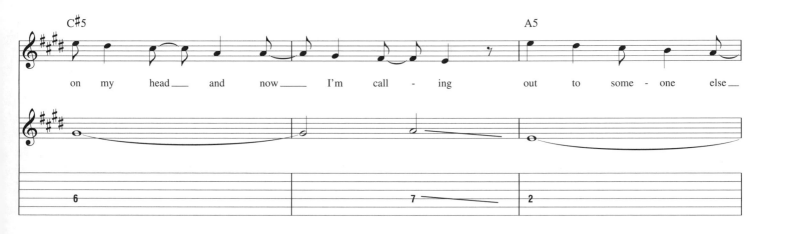

on my head ___ and now ___ I'm call - ing out to some - one else ___

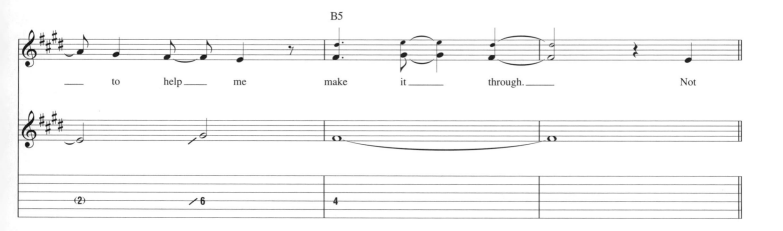

___ to help ___ me make it ___ through. ___ Not

Bridge

Gtr. 1 tacet
Gtrs. 2 & 3: w/ Rhy. Figs. 2 & 2A

ev - 'ry - bod - y knows that ev - 'ry - bod - y goes to a bet - ter place. ___

And not ev - 'ry - bod - y knows that ev - 'ry - bod - y could be liv - ing

their last days. ___ But the hard times will come ___

___ and we'll keep mov - ing on. We're mov - ing on.

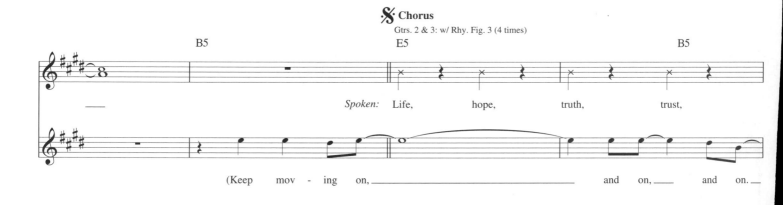

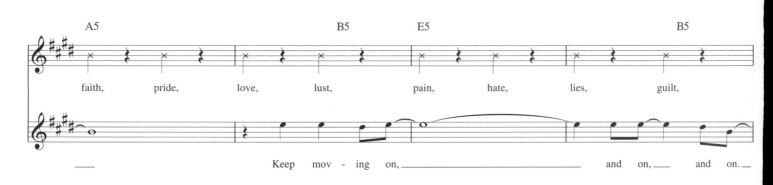

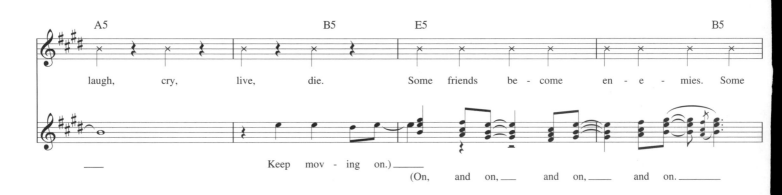

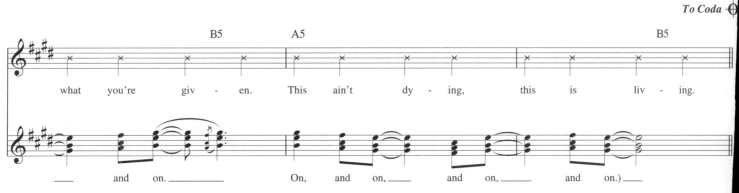

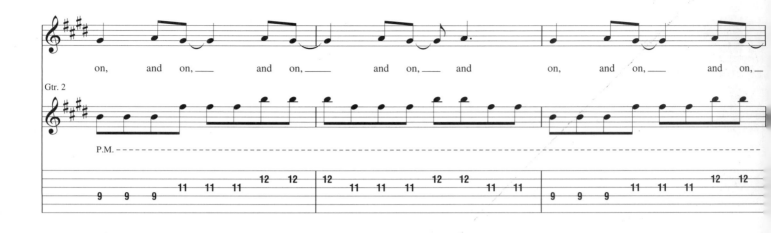

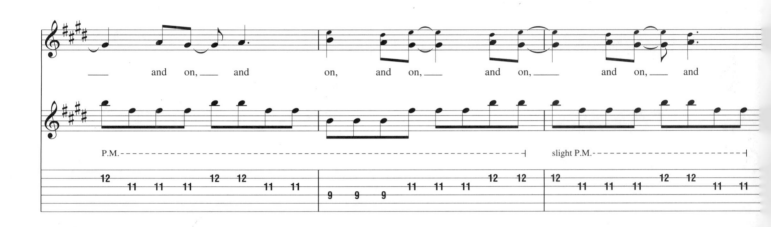

D.S. al Coda

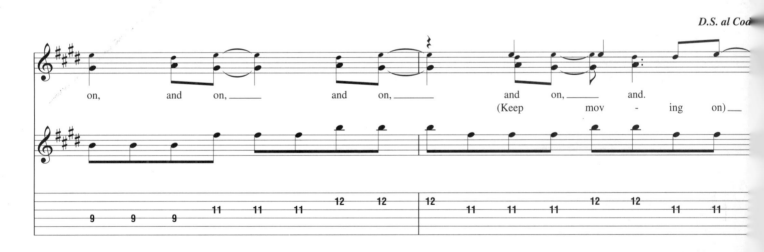

✛ Coda

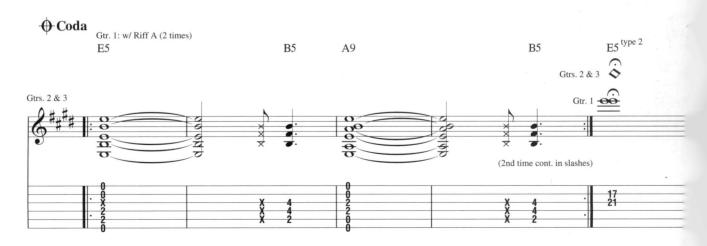

120